QUANTITATIVE
NATURALISTIC
RESEARCH

An Introduction to Naturalistic
Observation and Investigation

JOHN M. BUTLER, Ph.D.
University of Chicago

LAURA N. RICE, Ph.D.
University of Chicago

ALICE K. WAGSTAFF, Ph.D.
Duquesne University

In collaboration with

SARAH COUNTS KNAPP, Ph.D.
Napa State Hospital
Napa, California

PRENTICE-HALL, INC., ENGLEWOOD CLIFFS, NEW JERSEY

PRENTICE-HALL INTERNATIONAL, INC., *London*
PRENTICE-HALL OF AUSTRALIA, PTY., LTD., *Sydney*
PRENTICE-HALL OF CANADA, LTD., *Toronto*
PRENTICE-HALL FRANCE, S.A.R.L., *Paris*
PRENTICE-HALL OF JAPAN, INC., *Tokyo*
PRENTICE-HALL DE MEXICO, S.A., *Mexico City*

Library of Congress Catalog Card Number: 63-10538

Printed in the United States of America

PREFACE

A decade ago we began working on the problem of analyzing psychotherapeutic interviews. As time passed and as solutions to our
research problems emerged, we began to realize the solutions had
general implications. Going from the specific to the general carries
within it the danger of tunnel vision but sometimes has the advantage
of conferring uniqueness of perspective. It also has the realistic
advantage of being grounded in actual research problems.

In our view a fundamental emphasis in the following essay is the
insistence on faithful representation of subject behavior over periods
of observation. This may be contrasted with the usual transformation of behavior to scores in which information is discarded and in
which one draws the first step away from actuality.

A second fundamental emphasis is on analyzing the representation
of behavior with a minimum of assumptions. Although powerful
and sophisticated mathematical techniques related to those discussed
in this work exist, they seemed to us to require assumptions we were
unwilling to make or to require analysis of but a fraction of the data.
Thus the advantages of the use of distribution functions and of significance levels were, for us, offset and we were persuaded to follow
our own path.

As we proceeded in our search for a solution to our problems, the
analysis of naturalistic data came to be viewed as a kind of factor
analysis of behavior representations rather than of scores. If it is
a truism that one gets out of factor analysis what one puts into it,
it is also true (if not a truism) that factor analysis often informs our
understanding of what actually was put into the mill of routine
eventuating in what is symbolized by "factors." It is so with representations of behavior. What amounts to a kind of factor analysis

results in classes of behavior which may appropriately be called "factors." These mathematical partitions may serve as a ground for hypothesis formation, psychological induction and further, more refined study.

We conceive of the process of naturalistic observation and analysis as involving observation, the representation of the results of observation, analysis of the representation and the creation of a new framework for observation and further analysis culminating finally in rather formal hypotheses, theories and controlled experimentation. Methodologically our essay may be characterized as factor analytic or Thurstonian; logically, as Baconian; and procedurally as Darwinian or naturalistic.

The presentation presupposes an understanding of factor analysis in the tradition established by L. L. Thurstone and an understanding of matrices and vectors covered by a substantial portion of, say, the first three chapters of S. Perlis' *Theory of Matrices*. Nearly all of the mathematical statements are very common currency, so it was considered unnecessary to offer much in the way of mathematical proof and development. No mathematical buttressing of the point of view offered is intended or given. For our purposes the mathematics was subordinate and had the status of hammers, screwdrivers and other homely but necessary tools.

Although our use of the methods to be described has been limited to the analysis of psychotherapeutic interviews, we can envisage other uses by clinical and counseling psychologists, social psychologists, content analysts, comparative psychologists observing organisms in relatively free situations and, perhaps, taxonomists.

The authors have been most deeply influenced by some of the illuminating early papers of Professor Louis Guttman, by the factor analytic approach of the late Professor L. L. Thurstone and by the concept of identifiability enunciated by Professor Tjalling Koopmans. The list of references, with the exception of the references to latent class analysis, is limited to the work directly influencing our thinking.

We wish to express our appreciation to the Ford Foundation for allocating funds making our investigations possible, to thank Mr. L. Harmon Hook for the mathematical aid and advice he so generously afforded us and to thank Professor Jack Sawyer for careful and critical reading of two manuscript versions.

We are also indebted to the American Psychological Association for permission to reprint the discussion on pages 178–184 and the tables on pages 196–198 of Volume II of *Research in Psychotherapy*, edited by Drs. Lester Luborsky and Hans H. Strupp.

CONTENTS

CHAPTER ONE

      INTRODUCTION   1

CHAPTER TWO

      THE ANALYSIS OF EMPIRICAL CLASSIFICATION

      SYSTEMS   11

CHAPTER THREE

      VARIATIONS ON THE S MATRIX AND WEIGHTS FOR

      SUBJECTS   47

CHAPTER FOUR

      ORTHOGONAL BASES APPROXIMATING AN OBLIQUE

      SIMPLEST BASIS   54

CHAPTER FIVE

      HIGHER ORDER MATRICES AND VECTORS   63

CHAPTER SIX

      APPLICATIONS   67

APPENDICES

      A: TESTS OF SIGNIFICANCE FOR THE NUMBER OF

      BASIS VECTORS   92

      B: PROOF THAT THE SEQUENCE OF MATRICES,
      $R_a, R_1, \ldots, R_n$ CONVERGES TO AN I MATRIX
      (L. Harmon Hook)   95

      C: THE SPECIAL CASE OF THE DICHOTOMY   102

      D: ANALYSIS OF WEIGHTED DATA VECTORS   106

    REFERENCES   114

CHAPTER ONE

INTRODUCTION

When one considers the philosophy and teaching of science, it seems significant that little, if any, formal attention is paid to naturalistic observation and research, although it is quite clear that they consti- tute the foundation of all science. The science of physics is pro- foundly indebted to the uncontrolled observations of superstitious Babylonian and Chaldean priests. Recently we have witnessed widespread observances of the centennial of the masterwork of naturalistic observation and research, the Darwinian theory of evolution, which is still revolutionizing our concept of the biological world and, indeed, of ourselves. Yet in many current discussions of science by philosophers or by scientists in the role of philosophers, we find a great deal of emphasis placed upon what are considered to be the two major aspects of science: experimental method and logic, and the personal element, the latter being discussed under such headings as "genius", "creativity", "scientific imagination", and "luck".

Although scientific method is greatly admired, it seems that the practitioner of scientific method, the experimental scientist, is not. The skilled experimentalist at best attains second rank as a scientist; the highest rank he can hope to attain is that of Boyle. The deepest admiration is reserved for the Newtons, Einsteins, Darwins, and Flemings who are considered to be geniuses or to be lucky discoverers able to capitalise on the significance discerned in accidental events. Understanding science by division into the two aspects of objective method or verification and personal subjective elements creates a rather uncomfortable situation for the majority of scientists who do not possess genius and who realise that luck is a synonym for chance.

The sense of discomfort increases if one is in a borderline science, if one is exploring a field in which basic and fruitful concepts like those of Einstein, of Newton, and of Darwin have not been formulated; where experimentation, as in certain areas of psychology, seems to be reduced to empty formalism because positive knowledge does not exist which tells us what should be controlled.

When a scientist enters into an inquiry in a new domain, his ideas, however precise as ideas, are hazy with respect to the domain simply because it is an unexplored area. When the phenomena under consideration are not described well, when relationships at the phenomenal level are not known, the person who insists on starting out with precise experiments lacks the imagination required to observe, to look around and see, at the first level, what seems to be going on. Experiments which precede rather than succeed observation amount to being precise about vagueness and suggest a disproportionate concern for the opinions of other scientists with a disproportionate lack of concern for truth which, above all, should characterize the scientist. It is obvious that the scientist who wishes to bring a particular domain under the control of scientific law should attempt to observe and to arrive at preliminary hypotheses or systems of hypotheses on the basis of his observations. His ultimate aim, of course, should be identical to that of any other scientist, namely, to generate sets of propositions which, at crucial points, are verifiable through the processes of scientific method. His immediate aim then should be to arrive at fruitful hypotheses.

In our present stage of understanding science the creation of fruitful hypotheses must await the moment of insight of the genius or the lucky event which only the genius appreciates. Nevertheless, as psychological experimentation has shown quite clearly, the appropriate arrangement of situations can lead to insight into situations or can retard and prevent the occurrence of insight. The aim here will be to describe an approach to data of naturalistic observation which, it is hoped, will encourage the development of fruitful hypotheses with respect to the domain of inquiry.

NATURALISTIC OBSERVATION

As conceived here, the naturalistic observer approaches his domain of inquiry, considered to be some behavioral situation, with several sets of convictions, beliefs, frames of reference, biases, prejudices, call them what you will, which will hereafter be called a classification system. To a first approximation, at least, the observer knows what behavior is. That is, he has a definition, explicit or implicit, of what behavior is, and he knows in a preliminary way what behavior he is interested in observing. Suppose that he observes a single organism's behavior on a series of occasions and that each occasion covers a period of time such that several behaviors are observed. Then the observer has collected two sequences of observations, the sequence within occasions, and the sequence of occasions. It seems to be a reasonable assumption that if the observer is to formulate some hypotheses based on the organism's behavior, he will consider the behavior within occasions. And he will consider not only what does occur, but what does not occur that could be expected to occur. Also, he will note the sequence of various actions, or the absence of such a sequence, at each point in the course of the particular period of behavioral observation. Such considerations might lead to conclusions or hypotheses about what might be called the behavioral structure of an occasion. But there is also a sequence of occasions. Therefore, there will be a set of occasions, each having its own structure. The set of occasions constitute the data of our naturalist. The naturalist undoubtedly takes into account not only the sequence of occasions, but tries to see relationships among the behaviors over the whole set of occasions without regard to the structure of each occasion. If the naturalist is observing many behaviors over many occasions, his observations can aggregate to an impressive number, a number which can easily aggregate to an overwhelming amount as the number of organisms observed increases.

Suppose what probably is actually seldom the case, that the categories of observations of the naturalist are mutually exclusive. Were this so, it could and will later be shown that the nature of classification systems is such that it might well appear to the observer that there is order in the data in the sense that scientists think of order as of "underlying relations." Also, from well known experimentation in psychology on memory, learning, and forgetting, it is clear that the classification system of the observer may change continually as observation proceeds, so that the very process of observation may be, and really always is, conditioned by the preceding observations. Thus, the very process of data formation, from one point of view, changes. From another point of view it can be said that the classification system of the observer is continually conditioned by the observations. Thus we see that all is in flux, the observer has a frame of reference which is not fixed, which can change as a result of the very process of observation. Furthermore, what we know about memory indicates that additional changes in the frame of reference, and of the data conceived as the ordering of observation into the frame of reference of the observer, come about as a function of time. Bartlett's fascinating study of remembering indicates, that upon reflection after the events, the inner nature of the events seems to have changed.

Consider that naturalistic observer, the psychotherapist. Essentially, he observes the communicative or linguistic behavior of a patient or group of patients over periods of perhaps hundreds of therapy hours. Therefore, even were his classification sub-classes few in number and mutually exclusive, the observations would amount to a really overwhelming array of data. Even when the psychotherapist takes notes, no matter how voluminous, they are, at best, aids to memory. The therapist, a Freud for example, then must remember over long periods of time and in terms of a large number of patients, what happened, what did not happen, etc., in addition to considering information not obtained in the therapy hours. Then he creates on what he conceives to be his observations, a theory of psychotherapy and a psychological theory of personality. No matter how plausible and convincing these theories may be, it is clear that the interaction of observer and observed, the personal or subjective element, can and probably does play a large part in the creation of the theory – and in such a way that we do not know to what extent the theories describe the theorist or the patients.

It would indeed be a humbling and corrective experience for a psychotherapist to have copies of the original situations, such as sound recording or sound motion pictures, played back after a case description and analysis. For he would undoubtedly discover that, while there were "essential truths" in his formulation, what was described as having a dramatic unity had, in fact, far less unity, and was much more scattered throughout the observations than his formulations indicated. And he would also find that what on listening or viewing seemed to be important events, had been neglected in his formulation. In other words, faithful copies of the events lead, upon presentation to the original observer, to a change in the classification system or hypotheses consequent upon his original observation. Even were the psychotherapist unbiased or uninvolved, the case would be the same because of the large number of varied responses displayed by his patient.

The considerations outlined above suggest the function and problems of naturalistic observation. The function of naturalistic observation is to generate hypotheses concerning the underlying structure of behaviors, if any; it is not to test hypotheses. The testing of hypotheses is in the province of experimental methodology and, in certain situations, of statistical methodology. Generally speaking, the use of experimental method depends upon control, and by control is meant the control of *relevant* conditions or variables. Seldom, if ever, can everything be controlled. Thus, the use of experimental method depends upon previous positive knowledge or upon insight gained in uncontrolled situations. But uncontrolled situations are just those covered by naturalistic observation. Hence, if we can improve naturalistic observation, we are more likely to be in a position to have insight into what should be controlled in advancing an experimental expedition into the domain of inquiry.

The function of naturalistic observation being the generation of hypotheses, one basic problem posed by such observation is immediately apparent. It is what might be called objectifying the observations or moving from the act of observation to the recording of data. The recording of data is thought of as obtaining a record of behavior in symbolic form; getting such data implies:

1. a standard definition of what constitutes a response.

2. a classification scheme or system into which responses are placed as they occur.

In what follows it will be assumed that the investigator has a standard and specifiable definition of a response.

The function of the classification system in naturalistic observation and analysis is to provide an objective record of behavior such that, once the period of observation has ended, one can tell with certainty what was observed. Therefore, the classification should be objective in the sense that two observers would essentially classify behavior the same way; the classification scheme should be specifiable and reliable. To the extent that it is not, the classification system is personal and unreliable. Secondly, the classification system should have mutually exclusive sub-categories unless the classifying behavior of the investigator is the object of investigation. When the classes are not mutually exclusive, cross-classification may be dependent; some of the possible cross-classifications will be mere artifacts.

It seems that reliability and mutually exclusive sub-classes represent minimal characteristics of a satisfactory classification system. A reliable classification system with mutually exclusive classes would provide an objective record of behavior over a series of observations and would push the problems of subjectivity and insight back where they belong, namely, into the creation of the classification system itself and to the generation of hypotheses based upon analysis of the classified behavior. Since the number of classified behaviors or data may be very large, it seems that an additional criterion of a minimally satisfactory classification system would be that it be susceptible to objective analysis, preferably analysis of a type which treats the classification system and the data as a unit.

The three criteria of a minimally satisfactory classification system by no means exhaust the problems inherent in classifying behavior. For it is clear that an arbitrary number of classification systems can be applied in the same observational situation. And the same applies to the definitions of response. When we have two different universes of discourse, connected, possibly, only by a standard definition of response, two criteria of the relative validity of the systems might be called internal productivity and external productivity; internal productivity being some index of the amount of order in the behavioral data and external productivity being some index or set of indices indicating relationships between the behavioral data and other data. A somewhat analogous distinction is made in mental test theory between the kind of validity described by the correlation between a test and the factor (or factors) it represents and the kind of validity described by the correlation between a test and an external variable. Given two classification systems, the first having more internal and external productivity than the second, it seems clear that the first is preferable to the second. It should be noted, however, that one system might have more internal and less external productivity than the other and vice versa; the two criteria might not point to the same decision.

A further distinction to be made concerns the "grain" of the classification systems. A fine-grained system is one with relatively many sub-classes and a coarse-grained system, one with relatively few (and as few as two) categories. A system with only two sub-classes has, in effect, only one, since a two-class system can describe, at most, only one kind of organism-environment transaction, all other kinds being lumped together in the remainder class. Thus the two-class system represents the ultimate in coarse-grained systems for, of course, a one-class system is completely determined. A completely determined system can yield no information. Since the behavior of organisms is complex, it would seem that a three-class system, and other relatively coarse-grained systems would be less likely to be productive, other things being equal, than relatively fine-grained systems. Fine-grained systems are less likely to have responses classified into the remainder class.

In coarse-grained systems, behavior is likely to be classified into the remainder class because attention is centered on a few kinds of behavior; in fine-grained systems, however, such classifications are likely to be made because of inability to identify the class into which to order the response. In such a case the class "unclassifiable" becomes a sub-class of the remainder class. In actual investigations it is probably desirable to record, in addition to the explicitly defined categories, the unclassifiable and remainder classes, for they will often be of considerable interest and could yield valuable information.

A criterion related to that discussed above is exhaustiveness. An exhaustive system is one in which all responses are classified into explicit categories. It seems reasonable to suppose that the more exhaustive a system is, the more productive it is likely to be.

In general then a satisfactory classification scheme will have mutually exclusive sub-classes, be susceptible to routine analysis, and possess internal and external productivity. Productivity is in turn likely to be dependent upon "grain" and exhaustiveness. These rather rough, ready, and commonsensical criteria are somewhat vague and lack the sense of closure obtained by means of a complete intellectual scheme. However, they do seem to be serviceable criteria and can be used to some extent for developing a classification system before observation formally begins. Some of the criteria, especially productivity, will be delineated more sharply later.

One should remember that the behavior being considered here is completely uncontrolled by the investigator. Nevertheless, the classification system is somewhat analogous to a control of behavior in the sense that the observer insists on observing the behavior in terms of the classification system employed. Thus the observer is controlling his experience, as in an experiment, but, perhaps, in an undesirable manner. That is, his classification scheme may simply be an objectified set of prejudices having much to do with the misguided imagination of the observer but containing no insight about the kind of organism observed. In this case, it is likely that analysis of the data will reveal only the folly of the originator of the classification system. A properly conceived and executed experiment, however, does not fail to yield real information. This is in the very nature of the process of experimentation. Therefore, the naturalistic observer must be as carefully imaginative as possible in constructing his classification system; he must fuse his creativity and experience for the purpose of constructing a more than minimally satisfactory classification system.

The desirability of extreme care and maximal creativity in constructing a classification system can be seen by considering a situation in which behavior is physically controlled by limiting the behavior of the organism to series of finite alternatives. The maze in which the organism is restricted to right and left turn behavior is a good example; so are Fabrés caterpillars endlessly circling the post on which he placed them. Such simple situations, hardly to be conceived as constituting full experimental control, have yielded a wealth of information about response acquisition and instinctive behavior. Now in the maze, for example, the alternatives can be considered as a two-class classification system and analysis of the sequence of alternatives expressed in the behavior of the organism can be handled, as will be shown later, in the same manner as with the classification systems which do not imply the imposition of physical limitations upon the behavior of the organisms being observed. To make the point in a rather fanciful manner, when the organism is merely observed, the organism "selects" as behavioral alternatives the subclasses of the observer's classification system. When there is more control, choices are forced upon the organism by environmental conditions imposed by the investigator. In neither case is it remarkable that a "choice" is made. In the first case, however, "selection of alternatives" may have little to do with the organism observed and much to do with the observer. In the second case, selection of alternatives actually represents transactions however "artificial" the environment may be. In other words, in the second case the behavior represents an actual organism-environment transaction. In the first case the classified behavior *may* show only that behavior occurred; the classifications may not represent any actual transaction between organism and environment. This is the defect of uncontrolled observation; it may not be observation of more than the fact that responses occurred a given number of times; hence the necessity for the basic criterion of productivity. For productivity guards against just the possibility that a given classification system is irrelevant to a given group of organism-environment transactions or responses; it is here conceived that an irrelevant but specifiable and reliable classification system would, for a given set of responses, be unproductive; that is to say, an irrelevant system would result in data exhibiting no order.

SUMMARY

Exploratory investigations are necessary, and are most likely to be useful, when fruitful and basic concepts do not exist with respect to the domain of inquiry. Exploratory investigation almost necessarily starts with the expectation that underlying the manifold events in a domain of inquiry is an order; that a set of constructs will unify and simplify comprehension of a class of phenomena. When the scientific knowledge or the insight necessary for controlled experimentation is not at hand, the investigator can use naturalistic observations of the domain as a means of increasing his insight. By this means he may successively extend his insights to the point where controlled experimentation becomes possible and desirable.

In the behavioral domain of inquiry, naturalistic observation requires a definition of response and the application of a classification system to the responses observed. The classification system must, in order to be applied, have mutually exclusive categories and be reliable, capable of yielding the same results upon re-classification by a second observer. Since a given classification system cannot be considered to be unique, the problem of the worth or validity of the system arises. Worth (or validity) can be assessed in terms of internal and external productivity. External productivity cannot exist unless internal productivity also exists. The converse is not true. Productivity is more likely when classification systems are relatively fine-grained and exhaustive. Finally, a preferred classification system is one so formulated that its data, the behavior described in terms of the system, can be analyzed in an objective fashion, the analysis preferably being of the data considered as a whole.

A naturalistic investigation is concluded when analysis of the data results in a demonstration that the system is unproductive or productive as the case may be. If the system is productive the end result should be a sharpened and refined set of hypotheses leading to a better classification system with which to approach the domain. Or it may result in a set of hypotheses so refined as to indicate what is to be controlled and varied in an experimental attack upon the domain of inquiry.

The nature of exploratory investigation being what it is, it starts and ends with personal creation. Usually personal creation, the subjective element, pervades the entire process, often to the detriment of the investigation. The personal, subjective element should be confined to the beginning of the investigation when the classification system is being devised and made explicit and to the end when the routines of analysis have provided the formal results upon which personal creativity should operate.

CHAPTER TWO

THE ANALYSIS OF EMPIRICAL
CLASSIFICATION SYSTEMS

The purpose of a naturalistic analysis of behavior data is to find a structure of relations among the data serving as a basis for hypothesis formation. More accurately perhaps, one should speak of hypothesis reformulation since the classification system itself is a system of hypotheses. Prerequisite to finding the structure of relations is the representation of the classified data and the assessment of internal productivity. When a classification system has been judged to be internally productive, one then proceeds to ascertaining the structure of relations in the data. In practice, assessment of internal productivity and determination of structural relations may proceed simultaneously. However, the former is logically prior to the latter. Logically, the manner in which data is represented is a matter of choice. But logic is not science and it is only logically speaking that one can be arbitrary. In the behavioral domain, data comes in sequence; responses are made one after the other. Thus, if an individual organism is busily making responses, to each of which a number of some sort can be attached; then the organism in mathematical terms can be considered to be engaged in constructing an ordered n-tuple of numbers. An ordered n-tuple is a vector and the particular behavior vector for a particular organism is then a representation of the behavior of the organism. In the point of view taken here, the data of the investigator are the behavior vectors and the data are representations of acts of observation within a classification system. Parenthetically, it is our belief that all acts of observation are embedded in a classification system and that the concept of observation and the concept of classification are indivisible.

Basic, then to the problem of ascertaining structural relations among data is the problem of coding data in such a manner that the coding represents behavior as it occurs. The representation must show not only what occurred but when it occurred. This prescription rules out many schemes of representation of behavior such as the conventional item-score matrix of mental test theory and the representation of so-called response patterns by vectors which are either identical or have zero inner products, i.e., are orthogonal. Such representations may be formally impeccable but materially represent decisions to ignore part of the behavioral data in some way. Such decisions should have more than a formal basis. In any event, such decisions represent some kind of operation upon the data.

ARRANGEMENT OF DATA

Given a classification system with q mutually exclusive categories of responses applied to t organisms over n responses, with a unit entry denoting the occurrence of response number m into category number p for organism j, the classified behavior of the jth organism can be represented as a column matrix

$$s_{ij} = \text{col } (0, 0, \ldots, 1, \ldots 0_q, 1, 0 \ldots ,$$

$$0, \ldots 0_q, 0, 0, \ldots , 0, 0 \ldots , 1_p) \qquad (1)$$

where there are n unit entries, one for each response, and $n(q - 1)$ zero entries; that is, a total of nq rows. A fictitious data matrix where $n = 8$, $q = 2$, and $t = 25$ is shown in Table 1. This fictitious data matrix shows just what responses were observed as being made and when, in the sense of succession, by each subject. Such a matrix is the result of observing and classifying the behavior of 25 subjects, the behavior being regarded as discriminable into eight responses and the responses being regarded as discriminable into two sub-classes. The data matrix in the form shown gives the "natural history" of the behavior exhibited by the subjects over the period of observation. The data matrix S will be said to represent the behavior in fundamental form. It may be remarked that other representations of

TABLE 1

FICTITIOUS DATA MATRIX S

	Responses ($n = 8$)								Subjects ($t = 25$)									Subclasses ($q = 2$)							
	1	2	3	4	5	6	7	8	9	10	11	12	13	14	15	16	17	18	19	20	21	22	23	24	25
1	1	1	1	0	0	0	0	0	0	1	1	1	1	1	0	0	1	1	1	1	0	0	1	1	1
2	0	0	0	1	1	1	1	1	1	0	1	1	0	0	1	1	0	0	0	0	1	1	0	0	1
3	0	0	0	0	0	0	0	1	1	1	0	0	1	1	0	0	1	1	1	1	1	1	0	0	0
4	1	1	1	1	1	1	1	0	0	0	1	1	0	0	1	1	1	0	0	0	1	0	1	1	0
5	1	0	0	1	1	1	0	0	0	1	0	0	1	1	1	1	1	1	1	1	0	1	1	1	1
6	1	1	1	1	0	0	1	1	1	0	1	1	0	1	1	0	0	0	0	0	1	0	0	0	1
7	0	1	1	0	0	0	1	0	0	1	0	1	1	0	0	1	1	1	0	0	0	0	0	0	0
8	0	0	0	1	1	1	0	1	1	0	1	0	0	1	1	0	0	0	1	1	0	1	1	1	0
9	1	0	0	0	0	0	0	0	0	1	0	1	0	0	0	0	0	0	1	1	1	0	0	0	1
10	0	1	1	1	1	1	1	1	1	0	0	0	0	1	0	1	1	1	0	0	0	1	1	1	0
11	1	0	1	0	1	0	0	0	0	0	1	0	1	0	1	1	0	0	0	0	1	1	0	0	1
12	0	1	0	1	0	1	1	1	1	1	0	1	0	0	0	0	1	1	1	1	0	0	1	1	0
13	1	0	1	0	1	1	0	0	1	1	1	0	1	1	1	1	0	0	0	0	1	1	1	0	1
14	0	1	0	0	0	0	1	1	0	1	0	1	0	1	1	0	1	1	1	1	0	0	0	1	0
15	1	1	1	1	1	1	1	0	1	0	1	0	1	0	0	1	1	1	1	1	1	1	0	0	1
16	0	0	0	1	0	0	0	1	0	1	1	1	1	0	0	0	0	0	0	0	0	0	1	1	0

behavior classified into a finite number of mutually exclusive categories could be used. However, all such classifications can be brought into fundamental form. More precisely, the other representations, when put into matrix form, can be expressed as linear combinations of the vectors of S, but the matrices derived from other modes of representation will not yield the vectors of S. This is precisely why the S matrix is referred to as being in fundamental form.

ASSESSMENT OF INTERNAL PRODUCTIVITY

When the behavior of subjects has been coded and arranged in the form of the S matrix, the considerations outlined in the first chapter can be expressed in a more exact manner. For example, internal productivity can be assessed in terms of the randomness (or lack of it) of the distribution of responses. The chi-square statistic and its associated probability for a given level of significance may be regarded as a measure of internal productivity. The chi-square statistic is, however, a rather unsatisfactory measure of internal productivity. A more satisfactory measure is the ratio of the actual rank of S to the maximal possible rank. The rank of S will be less than the possible rank of S only when some of the rows or columns are identical. Such a situation will obtain only when the behavior of the subjects exhibits marked order or consistency and it is the order or consistency of response which indicates that the classification system is internally productive. The maximal possible rank of an $nq \times t$ S matrix representing the classified behavior of a group of subjects will be $(1 - 1/q)nq + 1$ or, equivalently, $nq - n + 1$. Each sub-matrix S_m, corresponding to the mth response, n_m, will have rank q, since for each response the sub-classes of the classification system are required to be mutually exclusive and each row vector of S represents one sub-class of the system. The requirement of mutual exclusivity of classification is shown in S_m by a set of q row vectors having zero inner products. A zero inner product thus indicates that the row vectors have no unit entries in common. Sub-matrix S_m may be regarded as defining a space of q dimensions containing a vector Y, with unit entries only whether or not it appears empirically; for the sum of the q rows of S_m is just the vector Y. There is one matrix S_m corresponding to each of the n responses. Therefore the sub-spaces defined by each of the responses have the Y vector in common. Since the rank of any $nq \times t$ matrix where $nq > t$ is at most nq, it follows directly that the rank of an $nq \times t\, S$ matrix is at most $nq - n + 1$. The maximal possible rank of S, $nq - n + 1$ is the mathematical counterpart of the requirement that the sub-classes of the classification system be mutually exclusive. If, for a given set of data, the actual rank of S is r, then the expression $r/(nq - n + 1)$, the rank differential, which may vary between $1/(nq - n + 1)$ and unity, may be used as one measure for assessing internal productivity. The value of $r/(nq - n + 1)$ will be less than unity only when some rows of S have identical placement of unit entries and when some rows have zero entries only. In this case a "preferential selection" of sub-classes of the classification system has been shown by the subjects. In a sense the "amount" of preferential selection is given by $r/(nq - n + 1)$, the rank differential, and the "kind" by the behavior sub-classes which are identical. When a maximum degree of "preferential behavior" is shown by the subjects, their behavior is maximally consistent; the rank of S will be unity and the behavior of all subjects will be identical. When the behavior of sub-groups of subjects is identical within sub-groups, the behavior of each of the groups being different, the corresponding S matrix will show r distinct groups of row (or column) vectors. The vectors of the ith group will be identical, and the inner products of the vectors in the ith and the jth groups respectively will be zero. If r vectors, one from each group, are selected, the r vectors form an orthogonal basis for the r-dimensional vector space defined by S and all subjects can be discriminated or classified perfectly in terms of the r vectors so chosen. Maximum discrimination in classification is then achieved when, for rank r of S, r orthogonal row vectors of S exist. It should be noted that for a classification system with q mutually exclusive sub-classes, there can be no more than q orthogonal row vectors in S. Thus, maximal internal productivity for a given classification system implies that the associated S matrix has rank of at most q and that there be at most q orthogonal row or column vectors in S. Many different sets of r orthogonal row or column vectors of S may exist; i.e., there are many different arrangements. When the rank of S is greater than q, the data will be said to have an oblique structure in the sense that, given a basis of empirical data vectors, at least $r - q$

of the vectors of the basis must have non-zero inner products with each other and with the q orthogonal vectors. The non-zero inner products indicate less than maximum discrimination between empirical classes of behavior and, consequently, less than optimum internal productivity of the classification system. *Internal productivity of the classification system is thus related not only to reduction in rank (the rank differential) but to the inner products of vectors from S chosen as a basis.* The higher the inner products between the unit basis vectors, the less internally productive the classification. Nevertheless, a given S matrix may have rank greater than q thus having an oblique data structure, but have high, though less than maximal, internal productivity.

Implicit in the above discussion is the restriction of the basis to empirical data vectors taken from S. The reason for the restriction is that the classes of behavior represented by the row vectors of S chosen for the basis are empirical classes and the structure of the data can then be described in terms of actually observed classes of behavior. To this restriction should be added the restriction that the co-ordinates of all data vectors be non-negative. These restrictions amount to confining the universe of discourse to what might be called the behavior space, which, as Table 1 clearly shows, must have like-signed entries when behavioral events of specified kinds are regarded as occurring or not occurring.

The restriction that unit length basis vectors be normalizations of data vectors and that the coordinates of the data vectors be non-negative results in a unique orthogonal basis when the rank, r, of S is equal to or less than q. This is the case in which there are r groups of vectors; within each group the vectors are identical and have identical inner products. The inner product of any two vectors in the ith and jth groups is zero; the sub-classes of response do not intersect. Any change of basis then results in a basis such that the matrix of coordinates of the data vectors contains negative entries which cannot be interpreted in behavioral terms. It seems then that the restriction to non-negative coordinates is not merely arbitrary. When $r > q$, the data structure must be oblique in the sense that $r - q$ of the basis vectors must have non-zero inner products and the obliqueness of the structure reflects less than maximal internal productivity in the classification system. That is, the discrimination among subjects in terms of the sub-classes of behavior is less than optimal.

When a data basis is oblique, complex problems arise in interpretation of the matrix of coordinates of the data vectors because of the non-zero inner products of the basis vectors which indicate that ambiguities are present in the data and in the classification system. Thus the process of hypothesis formation, based on regarding the basis vectors as being generators of the data, becomes more complex. One way to circumvent this difficulty is to use the oblique data basis to define an orthogonal basis which "best" fits the data basis. Then the behavior classes defined by the vectors of the orthogonal basis do not intersect and are independent. The orthogonal basis represents a non-empirical set of behavior classes strictly determined by the oblique basis and "most similar" to it. Depending on the actual goodness of fit, the matrix of coordinates of the data vectors expressed in the orthogonal basis will be similar to the matrix of coordinates expressing the data vectors in the oblique basis. The similarity insures that similar hypotheses will emerge from the consideration of each matrix and makes it possible to avoid the complex problems inherent in considering the relations between intersecting or overlapping behavior classes. It is perhaps unnecessary to mention that the configuration of data vectors is not changed by the change of basis. Hence accuracy is sacrificed for simplicity and clarity when a best fitting orthogonal basis is used for hypothesis formation in place of its corresponding oblique basis. Fortunately this is more a theoretical than a practical problem; generally the two matrices of coordinates will be so similar as to lead to similar interpretations. If, however, the data basis is oblique, and if the investigator can use the non-zero inner products in the process of hypothesis formation, he should by all means do so, for the data basis best represents the data for the purposes of inference.

THE BEST DATA BASIS

Many data bases can be derived from an S matrix, the vectors of which have an oblique structure; when the configuration of vectors is orthogonal, then the basis, under the restrictions previously stated, is unique. The unique orthogonal basis corresponds to perfect discrimination among subjects by the classification system and represents maximal internal productivity. Thus an orthogonal data basis is the best data basis since it corresponds to maximal internal productivity of the classification system.   In general, however, the rank of S will exceed q and then the vectors of any data basis will have non-zero inner products, and the system will have less than maximal internal productivity.

The question can now be asked: Which among the several possible oblique *data* bases is the best?   A preliminary answer to this question is that the coordinates of the data vectors of S be non-negative. Such a *data* basis corresponds to the intuitive notion of "outside" or "boundary" vectors.   Given a set of data vectors with cosines less than unity and lying in a two-space, it is clear there is just one *data* basis for which the coordinates of the data vectors are non-negative and that this basis is a basis of "outside" vectors.   However, it is not clear that in a higher dimensional space, there is just one basis of boundary vectors except in the case where the data basis is orthogonal.   In the latter case the basis vectors are boundary vectors no matter what the dimensionality.   Taken at unit length the orthogonal basis vectors comprise a collection of vectors B, such that the zero vector alone is orthogonal to the members of B.   Such a collection is called orthonormal complete: an orthonormal complete set of vectors is always a basis for B and the members of the orthonormal complete set always have inner products of unity or zero.   That the vectors of B are an orthonormal complete set implies that B is not contained in a larger set with members orthogonal to the members of B, for B is so defined that the zero vector alone is orthogonal to its members.   And the zero vector has zero length so is not a member of B.   Since the coordinates of the data vectors on the members of the orthonormal complete set, which form a basis for the vectors of S, are inner products, it follows that the sum of squares of the coordinates* for any vector is the self inner product of that vector and that

$$c = \frac{1}{nq} \sum_1^{nq} \sum_1^r \frac{a_{ij}^2}{h_i^2} = 1.00 \qquad (2)$$

where a_{ij} and h_i are the coordinates and the length of the ith vector respectively.

It can be shown that a value of unity for c is a criterion for orthonormal completeness, so when c is unity the vectors under considera-

---

*Coordinates are here defined as parallel projections of vectors on basis vectors.

tion are the vectors of an orthonormal basis. If c is less than unity for r linearly independent data vectors in a space of dimension r, the r basis vectors are not orthogonal. If S is of rank r with c less than unity for all bases with unit length vectors taken from S, the structure of S is such that no orthogonal data basis exists. From (2) it is clear that for every data basis there is a value of c; the largest value of c is here taken to define the "most nearly orthogonal basis." The more closely orthogonality is approximated, the less the intersection or overlap of the classes formed by the data vectors. In a collection of values of c, the largest value identifies the basis of vectors which corresponds to the intuitive notion of boundary or outside vectors. While it may be that given two values of c, c_i, and c_j, the coordinates of the data vectors expressed in the two bases associated with c_i and c_j are non-negative (there may be more than one set of boundary vectors), the larger value identifies the basis which discriminates the best among the subjects under consideration. A rule for finding the best data basis can now be formulated: Among the finite number of data bases for a given matrix, S, identify a basis for which c has the highest value.

For a given S matrix, there are nq data vectors. Therefore, the number of bases to be evaluated is $nq!/r! \, (nq - r)!$. It does not seem to be necessarily true that for a given matrix, S, there will be but one largest value of c. If there are, for a given case, two such largest values, there are two "best" data bases of r vectors each and r of the $2r$ vectors are, from the definition of a basis, linearly independent. If the vectors in the two bases are dependent, one by one, substitution of vectors from one set to another will not change c and the two bases are in fact identical. If the vectors of the two bases are not collinear, the vectors in one basis are combinations of two or more of the vectors in the other basis. Substitution of vectors from one set to another can then only decrease c, for all combinations of vectors have been used to get the largest value of c. Therefore, manipulation of the data cannot improve matters and cannot, therefore, resolve the indeterminacy. However, whether in fact, the indeterminacy exists for a given S matrix can be determined by finding all values of c. If there is but one basis corresponding to the higher value of c the most nearly orthogonal data basis has been identified.

THE MOST NEARLY INVARIANT SET OF COORDINATES

When a basis has been chosen it is hoped that the application of the classification system to additional samples of subjects will result in some kind of invariance for the original set of coordinates even though additional sub-classes may have been attached to the classification system. When the classification system has been applied to a new sample of subjects it may well be that the coordinates of the data vectors on the principal axes will be markedly different for the two samples because these axes are extremely sensitive to changes in the cosines of angles between vectors. Yet a kind of invariance may exist even though the cosines of the angles between the data vectors change. For example, those boundary vectors which are most nearly orthogonal, and which form a basis, are just those vectors on which some vectors, and at least $r - 1$ on each, will have zero coordinates. Also at least r vectors will have but one non-zero coordinate. Now those vectors having one non-zero coordinate define the basis vectors and these vectors reflect the most distinctly classified behaviors, that is; the behaviors most different from each other. Therefore, it is just those behaviors which would be required to change the most in order to render the matrices of the coordinates of the most orthogonal bases totally dissimilar. If, for example, the data structure of the first S matrix were orthogonal with rank r and the structure of the second were oblique with rank $s > r$, it could still be that a data sub-basis of r vectors in the second sample could yield a sub-matrix of coordinates of order $nq \times r$ similar to the $nq \times r$ matrix of coordinates in the first sample even though cosines between data vectors were different in the two samples.

Similarity between two $nq \times r$ matrices with rank r, F and F_1, say, can be assessed by the following means. Consider the equations which transform one matrix into another:

$$FX = F_1 \qquad (3)$$

where X is $r \times r$. Then pre-multiplying by F' and then by $(F'F)^{-1}$ gives

$$X = (F'F)^{-1} F'F_1 \qquad (4)$$

From (4) it can be seen that if F and F_1 are identical, then X is an identity matrix. If they differ by constants, X is a diagonal matrix. Further increase in dissimilarity is indicated by the appearance of non-zero off-diagonal entries in X. Thus if X is an identity matrix or a diagonal matrix, it can still be said that a degree of similarity obtains between F and F_1. Similarity between F and F_1 is what Thurstone (*Multiple Factor Analysis*, 1947, pp. 364-67) has called configurational invariance in factor matrices. A somewhat rough but still serviceable indicator of configurational invariance is given by the rank order correspondence of corresponding columns in F and F_1. Configurational invariance in "factor pattern" is given by similarity between F and F_1 in which values of unity have been substituted for non-zero values in F and F_1 and in which zero values have been given to zero entries regarded as being non-significant. For a non-negative matrix of coordinates, then, it is just those matrices which are generated by the most nearly orthogonal bases which are regarded as most likely to be invariant from sample to sample in the sense of likelihood of exhibiting similarity. If the goal of the investigator is to determine the most nearly invariant matrix of coordinates, then the most invariant data basis should be that which is "most nearly orthogonal." Such a data basis will hereafter be called a simplest basis. If the simplest basis is oblique and it is desired to use an orthogonal basis, an orthogonal basis best fitting the simplest basis should be found. Best fitting orthogonal bases are discussed in Chapter 4.

ANALYTICS OF THE SIMPLEST BASIS

The concept of the simplest basis, or equivalently the simplest matrix of coordinates, implies stability of data structure from sample to sample. It therefore also implies increasing stability of relationship with variates or criteria external to the classification system as one goes from the least invariant to the most invariant basis. The most invariant basis is expected to have the highest internal productivity over a range of samples; it is also expected to change the least from sample to sample. Given an S matrix with rank r and an orthogonal data structure, an orthogonal data basis is unique under the restriction of non-negative coordinates. For a specific S matrix with rank r and possessing an orthogonal data structure, there will be $s_1 \geq s_2 \geq \ldots \geq s_r$ data vectors collinear with each basis vector, the number of vectors in each group being s_i. For the sub-group of s_i vectors all non-zero coordinates will be identical. An orthogonal rotation of two or more of the basis vectors will result in a new matrix of coordinates such that there will be additional non-zero entries in the new matrix of coordinates. Length is invariant under orthogonal rotations so the new non-zero coordinates will be greater in absolute value than their counterparts in the original matrix of coordinates. As a result, reduced column variation in the new matrix will be one effect of the rotation.

Assume now that the vectors of S have been expressed in terms of the r principal axes of $(1/t)SS'$, a matrix of joint proportions, the data structure being oblique. In the space defined by the data matrix S, the unit vector on the first principal axis is the vector most similar to the data vectors; on the second, to those vectors in the $r - 1$ space orthogonal to the first principal axis and so on. In this sense, therefore, they are central vectors and the first principal axis may be regarded as the "central" vector for the data vectors. Each non-zero data vector has a non-zero inner product with the first principal axis so for oblique data structures only the zero vector is orthogonal to the axis whereas for an orthogonal data structure non-zero data vectors will be orthogonal to the axis. Each data vector is, therefore, in the plane of two or more principal axes except when the data vectors are collinear with the first principal axis. The sum of squares of the cosines of each data vector with the principal axes sum to unity and each squared cosine gives the proportion of the vector accounted for by the principal axis in question.

From the fact that the squared cosines of the ith vector of S with the principal axes sum to unity it follows that the vector for which the sum of the squared cosines on the $r - 1$ principal axes, excluding the first, is the greatest, is that vector which is least similar to the remaining data vectors. This vector will have the lowest squared cosine with the first principal axis and will be called the pivot vector. When there are squared cosines on the first principal axis with values less than $1/r$, these vectors will have at least one cosine on some other principal axis which is higher than that on the first. The pivot vector will be the vector in this group with the lowest cosine with the first principal axis and the vectors in this group with low intercosines are likely to be vectors of the most nearly orthogonal basis. Those vectors with squared cosines between $1/r$ and 0.5 may have a cosine on one of the remaining principal axes equal to or greater than their cosines with the first principal axis. Thus those vectors with cosines of .707 or less on the first principal axis comprise a group of vectors which may have cosines on the later principal axes which are equal to or greater than their cosine with the first. Within this group is a sub-group which must have one cosine on one of the $r - 1$ last principal axes greater than the cosine on the first principal axis. This group of vectors contains at least one boundary vector and is the group likely to contain all or most of them. By starting with the vector with lowest cosine on the first principal axis and values in the range from zero to $1/\sqrt{r}$, in the range $1/\sqrt{r}$ to .707, and in the range from .707 to .866, groups of vectors significantly and differentially related to the $r - 1$ last principal axes may be obtained.

The row vectors in the $nq \times r$ matrix of principal axes must have non-negative cosines with the first principal axis and both positive and negative non-zero cosines with the $r - 1$ last principal axes. Consider first only the positive cosines on the last principal axis and assume that there is a cosine which is the highest in its column and higher than other cosines, positive or negative, in its row. Then the data vector corresponding to this cosine is one of those least similar to the first principal axes and therefore to the other data vectors. Next assume another such cosine on each of the principal axes excluding the first. The result is $r - 1$ cosines, each corresponding to a data vector, each maximally related to orthogonal basis vectors, and each being accounted for less than 50% by the first principal axis. Another such set can be obtained, providing it exists in the data, by considering the highest negative cosines on the $r - 1$ last principal axes. The net result is $2(r - 1)$ data vectors, r of which are linearly independent, which are about as different as possible from the $nq - 2r + 2$ remaining data vectors. To this group of vectors may be added, if it is not already a member, the pivot vector, the vector with the lowest cosine with the first principal axis. We believe that this group of $2r - 1$ vectors will always contain the vectors of the simplest basis or bases as the case may be. However, we have found no way to prove that this belief is in fact true.

Since proof that the group of $2r - 1$ vectors discussed above actually always contain the simplest data basis is lacking, one cannot be sure that the basis finally picked is the simplest basis unless it is also known that it corresponds to the highest value of c. This can be computed routinely but at considerable cost in computation. The number of values of c or of the sums of intercosines of vectors in different bases to be computed may be reduced by noting that if the group of $2r - 1$ vectors does not contain all of the vectors in the simplest basis, it must contain most of them. This is guaranteed by the way in which selection insures that the $2r - 1$ vectors are collectively quite dissimilar to the other data vectors. One can proceed by taking those r vectors, including the pivot vector, of the $2r - 1$ vectors which have the lowest sum of intercosines. This is the most nearly orthogonal basis for the $2r - 1$ vectors. After determining the cosines of all data vectors with the vectors of the basis, a group of r clusters of vectors may be obtained by locating for each basis vector those vectors having higher cosines with the basis vector than with the first principal axis. Also they must have higher cosines with the basis vector than the basis vector has with the first principal axis. Taking values of c for various combinations of the pivot vector with the members of the clusters on the remaining basis vectors will identify the simplest basis.

Usually $2(r - 1)$ vectors cannot be found which meet the conditions specified above. However, setting the same conditions for the $r - 1$ principal axes excluding the first usually gives $2r - 1$ vectors from which the simplest basis may be selected, and at least r will be obtained. Since taking linear combinations of the vectors in clusters has the advantage of using more than one vector to define a basis, it is tempting to do so. However, such a basis will then generate a matrix of coordinates with negative entries. A basis derived from combinations of cluster vectors may, however, be advantageous if the investigator is going to use a matrix of coordinates on orthogonal basis vectors. Orthogonalizing on the basis derived from linear combinations of cluster vectors very similar to the vectors of the simplest basis will most likely produce a satisfactory orthogonal basis. However, there is still a risk of small negative coordinates, which would necessitate graphical orthogonal rotations.

When there are two or more bases corresponding to the highest value of c, the differentiating vectors in the different bases will usually have high inter-cosines. Therefore, taking linear combinations, say centroids, of the vectors differentiating the bases will give a satisfactory final solution, particularly if the final oblique basis is orthogonalized. In other words the value of c derived from the basis arrived at by taking linear combinations of the vectors differentiating the bases associated with the highest value of c will generally be very close to the highest value. In practice one can expect the association of the highest value of c with more than one basis to be unusual; more usually the simplest basis will be unique in the sense that it will be the only basis associated with the highest value of c. Another way in which to choose one from among different simplest bases is to find the sum of the variances of the coordinates on each basis vector. The basis corresponding to the highest sum of variances should then be selected as the final basis. If more than one simplest basis corresponds to the highest sum of variances, linear combinations of the vectors differentiating the bases may be used to obtain the final basis.

In the simplest data basis, r of the nq vectors have been selected for special emphasis. This is not in accord with the thinking of those who would rely on more than r vectors for establishing r basis vectors. However, approaches using more than r vectors to establish a basis have not been considered because of the restriction to non-negative entries in the matrix of coordinates which is the only type of matrix corresponding directly to the matrix of represented behaviors. The cluster approach and the principal axis approach may be modified so as to result in a final non-negative matrix of coordinates having direct behavioral meaning. Orthogonalizing on bases derived from clusters of vectors is the way in which such bases may be handled. The use of principal axis methods is described in the succeeding section.

The development to this point may be stated as follows: The simplest basis is that data basis expected to exhibit invariance or stability under additional sampling of responses of subjects, and under adding more categories to the classification system. Such invariance is expected for the same reasons that factorial invariance is expected in factor analysis. Lengthening the column vectors or the row vectors of S by additional sampling would require that the added unit entries so change the data structure that the vectors originally defining the structure become the longer vectors and that those which were originally longer vectors become the shorter vectors. Since the unit entries in the S matrix are determined by the behavior of subjects, additional subjects would necessarily have to be quite different in their behavior from the original subjects. If additional responses were to be sampled, change in data structure would mean a change in the subjects while they were observed. That this could happen cannot be denied, but that it would happen differentially for subjects from two samples under similar conditions seems unlikely.

The simplest data basis is that most nearly orthogonal, for which the coordinates are non-negative, and for which the value of c is the highest. When a data basis is associated with a unit value of c, the basis is orthogonal and unique; no other basis meeting the restriction of non-negative coordinates can then be obtained. When the highest value of c is less than unity, a kind of uniqueness can still obtain in the sense that just one basis is associated with the highest values. In this case the basis is oblique and is the most nearly orthogonal basis. When more than one basis is associated with the highest value of c, taking linear combinations of the vectors differentiating the bases provides a satisfactory resolution of the indeterminacy afforded by two or more simplest bases. The indeterminacy is resolved in the sense that a value of c for the final basis close to that of the highest value will be obtained. The value of c for the final data basis used may be viewed as a measure of internal productivity. It will be rare that more than one basis will be associated with a value of c so in practice the indeterminacy of basis will seldom be a problem.

A substitute for c entailing less in the way of computation is the index of internal productivity

$$\frac{1 - u}{r(r - 1)} \tag{5}$$

where u is the sum of the elements of the matrix of inner products of unit basis vectors and r is the number of vectors in the basis. When internal productivity is maximal, the index of internal productivity attains a value of unity; when internal productivity is nil, a value of zero.

WEIGHTED DATA VECTORS AND BASES

In considering the simplest data basis it can be seen that the variance of inner products on simplest bases will be near to a maximum value because they are maximally separated. That is, given a set of basis vectors which are orthogonal, vectors with cosines of unity with a basis vector, and other vectors with high cosines on the basis vector, will have zero to low cosines with other basis vectors. This will be true for vectors with high cosines with a basis vector. In the case in which all vectors are collinear with the vectors of an orthogonal basis, the variance of the cosines of the data vectors with the basis will be a maximum in the sense that the sum of the variances of the cosines on each basis vector will be a maximum. This is so because any rotation of basis vectors will result in additional non-zero cosines of data vectors with basis vectors and in the reduction of the higher cosines with a consequent reduction in variance. Consequently, it is to be expected that the sum of the variance of cosines of data vectors on simplest basis vectors will be near a maximum value and will be greater than similar variances for the great majority of data bases.

It could be that for some non-orthogonal basis which is not a simplest basis the sum of the variances of absolute values of parallel projections might be greater for the basis than for the simplest basis. This may be so when the vectors of the simplest basis are members of clusters of vectors with very high inter-cosines. But the difference in the sums of variances would not be great and the bases would in fact give similar matrices of coordinates, so similar in fact as to generate highly similar or identical hypotheses and interpretations.

The main point in the preceding discussion is that the simplest data basis is quite similar to that data basis with the greatest sum of variances of cosines on basis vectors. Hence the simplest basis is a data basis for which the data structure is, or nearly is, expressed in the simplest and most parsimonious way for a basis of r vectors.

When all data vectors are collinear with the vectors of an orthonormal basis, this simplest basis is the basis of unit principal axes.* This can be illustrated for the two-dimensional case by noting that it is desired to find the maximum value of

$$T = \sum_{1}^{n-m} (h_i \cos \theta)^2 + \sum_{1}^{m} (h_j \pi/2 - \cos \theta)^2$$

where n is the number of data vectors; m is the number of data vectors collinear with one of the basis vectors; $n - m$ is the number of data vectors collinear with the other basis vectors; θ is the angle between one of the basis vectors and the first principal axis; $\pi/2 - \theta$ is the angle between the other basis vector and the first principal axis and h_i and h_j are the lengths of the ith and the jth data vectors. The first derivative of T with respect to θ is $c \sin \theta \cos \theta$ where c is non-zero. The

*This was pointed out by Professor Charles Wrigley.

derivative can only be zero when $\sin \theta = 0$ or $\cos \theta = 0$. This can happen only when $\theta = 0$ or $\pi/2$. Solving with θ at zero and at $\pi/2$ gives the two extremum values.

In this ideal case the data structure is completely orthogonal and any orthogonal rotation of axes will reduce the sum of the variance of the coordinates on each basis vector. Also, introduction of new data vectors not collinear with the basis vectors will result in a new set of principal axes located nearer to the "center" of the configurations of vectors in the sense that they will more closely approximate the centroid axes than before. In this case of an oblique data structure, the principal axes will represent the data vectors in a highly complex manner rather than in the simple and parsimonious manner of the simplest basis. This will be reflected in the lesser sum of the fourth powers of the coordinates of the data vectors relative to the case in which, for the same number of data vectors with the same lengths as in the oblique case, the data vectors have a completely orthogonal structure.

Since it is those vectors making the configuration of data vectors oblique which locate the principal axes near the centroid axes, differential weights may be applied to the data vectors according to the obliqueness of the data structure so as to give more weight to boundary vectors and those vectors having high cosines with the boundary vectors than to vectors with low cosines with the boundary vectors. The vectors contributing most to the obliqueness of the data structure will in general be the longer vectors whereas boundary vectors and vectors with high cosines with the boundary vectors will tend to be the shorter vectors. It seems reasonable, therefore, to weight data vectors so as to relatively shorten the "central" vectors and relatively lengthen the "outer" or boundary vectors.

Expressing the inner product of each data vector with the principal axes as a cosine increases the variance of the coordinates along rows of the principal axis matrix as does using the squared cosine. However, the variance of the cosines squared is equal to or less than the variance of the cosines themselves. Similarly the expression p/p_k, where p is the sum of the latent roots and p_k is the kth latent root, has the effect of increasing column variation and increases it more than $1/\sqrt{p_k}$ or $1/p_k$. The cosines of data vectors on the principal axes are the proportions of the data accounted for by the axes when all vectors have been given equal weight and p_k/p is the proportion of the data accounted for by the kth principal axis. Therefore, among available constants, weighting directly by the cosines and inversely as the proportion of the data accounted for by the principal axes maximally increases row and column variation in the matrix of coordinates of data vectors on principal axes.

The effect of row weighting and column weighting is to greatly increase variation among the elements of the matrix. The increase in variation is differential with respect to single vectors. Those vectors with high cosines with the last principal axis will be relatively increased in length and those with high cosines with the first principal axis will be relatively decreased in length. Also the similarities and differences between pairs of vectors as measured by cosines will be accentuated differentially, the accentuation being most marked for those vectors lengthened the most. And in general those vectors lengthened the most will be the boundary vectors containing among them the vectors of the simplest basis or bases for the boundary vectors and will have the highest cosines with the $r - 1$ last principal axes.

Let

$$G = PP' \tag{6}$$

where P is the $nq \times r$ matrix of the coordinates on principal axes of R_0, the matrix of joint proportions, $(1/t)SS'$. Then G represents an approximation to R_0 based on the decision that enough basis vectors have been selected. Also G has rank r whereas the rank of R_0 is in general $nq - n + 1$. The r principal axes of G are the same as the first r principal axes of R_0 and P is a sub-matrix of the principal axes of R_0. Let D be a diagonal matrix with elements of normalizing constants for the rows of P, and K a diagonal matrix with elements p/p_k where p and p_k are the sum of the latent roots and the kth latent root, respectively. Then matrix DPK is a matrix of the proportions of unit data vectors giving the proportion of the data vector as represented in P accounted for by each principal axis weighted inversely as the proportion of the data vectors, (not in normalized form) accounted for by the principal axes. DPK is then such that the vectors with the highest cosines on the $r - 1$ last principal axes will become the longer vectors and those with the highest cosines on the first principal axis the shorter vectors.

Taking the principal axes of

$$DPKKP'D = L \tag{7}$$

gives the weighted data vectors expressed in terms of the matrix of their own principal axes, denoted by M. The $nq \times r$ matrix, M, will reflect to a certain degree a reversal of the roles of the principal axes of P. For example the last principal axis in M will have all or nearly all small non-zero coordinates and the vectors with high weights on the last two basis vectors of DPK will have especially significant roles in determining the first principal axis of L. Also the variation in coordinates will change greatly although the lengths of the vectors of DPK and of L will be the same. The highest absolute values of coordinates will be numbers such as, say, 10.5, whereas the zero and near-zero entries of DP will remain at zero and near-zero values in L. Thus it may be said that the boundary vectors in P will be accentuated the most in L. Yet all vectors participate in the formation of the principal axes of L.

It was conjectured earlier on the basis of factor analytic thinking and experience that the simplest data basis would be the most stable or most nearly invariant data basis under repeated sampling or increase in the number of responses sampled, or under additions to the classification system because the simplest data basis is similar to a simple structure basis under the restriction of non-negativity and of orthogonal or less than orthogonal bases. The simple structure solution in factor analysis is noticeably more stable or invariant under repeated sampling or the addition of new tests to the battery when compared, say, with the principal axis or centroid bases.

The simplest data basis and the simple structure bases usually depend upon rather small sub-collections of data vectors. On the other hand, the principal axes of L weight most heavily those vectors of the simplest data basis and those vectors having high cosines with them while at the same time being derived from all vectors. For this reason it seems likely that the $nq \times r$ matrix, M, of coordinates on the principal axes of L is the most stable or most nearly invariant matrix of coordinates obtainable from the data vectors while at the same time possessing the advantage of being unique. The uniqueness permits, therefore, a decision between bases when more than one unweighted data basis corresponds to the highest value of c. It seems also that the matrix of coordinates, M, provides a unique solution to the simple structure problem in factor analysis by reason of the fact that it must have factorial invariance if simple structure has factorial invariance and by reason of the fact that, given alternative simple structure solutions, the principal axes of L provide an objective basis for selecting one (or neither) of the solutions. An example of an analysis of data based on matrices L and M is given in Appendix D.

The sum of squares of the coordinates of the row vectors of M may be regarded as a measure of invariance. The measure of invariance is the same as that obtained by taking the sum of the squared coordinates of row vectors of DPK. A weighted, and better, measure may be obtained from M by multiplying each coordinate of the kth principal axis by the proportion of the kth latent root to the sum of the latent roots. In this way each row of elements of M is weighted by the invariance of the principal axes of L as well as by the invariance of the data vectors, those vectors having the highest weightings being the vectors with highest coordinates on the first principal axis.

Although the matrix M renders the selection of vectors having the highest invariance values susceptible to visual selection, computing routines for clustering the vectors may be employed. One such routine follows:

1. Select $2(r - 1)$ vectors from M by taking from each of the first $r - 1$ columns those row vectors with the highest positive and negative coordinates. Add to this group, if it is not already a member, the vector with the highest invariance value.

2. Compute cosines between members of the group of $2r - 1$ vectors. Since there will finally be r vectors of a basis $2r - 1 - r$ vectors will have relatively high cosines. Eliminate the $2r - 1 - r$ vectors by comparing cosines. Those vectors having high positive cosines with another vector are the candidates for elimination. Of two vectors having a high cosine, the vector with the lowest invariance value is to be eliminated.

3. With r linearly independent pivot vectors selected, compute cosines of all data vectors with the r pivot vectors. If any vector has a high cosine with a pivot vector and a higher invariance value than the pivot vector, it should replace the pivot vector. Also if any vector has low cosines on all of the r pivot vectors and a higher invariance vector than any one of them, it should replace the pivot vector with the lowest invariance value.

The final result is a set of r linearly independent pivot vectors which may be ordered in terms of their invariance values. A cluster can be sensibly defined as a group of vectors having higher positive cosines with the pivot vector than the pivot vector has with the principal axis on which the pivot vector has its highest cosine. A cluster so defined may contain vectors with relatively low invariance values. The cluster may be further delimited by requiring that the mean invariance value for the members of each cluster order the cluster in the same way as the invariance value of the r pivot vectors.

The row vectors of M may be weighted by using pivot vectors or by the use of clusters of vectors so as to obtain a final data basis for the weighted data vectors. Use of the pivot vectors gives a basis the individual members of which have the highest possible invariance values consistent with the dimensionality of the data space. The use of clusters results in basis vectors which are combinations of the vectors in each cluster, and thus have some advantage in statistical stability. The vectors in each cluster may be combined as follows:

1. Weight the row vectors in M corresponding to the ith cluster by the inner product of each row vector with the pivot vector.
2. Weight each row vector of the ith cluster by its weighted invariance value.
3. Sum all weighted vectors in the ith cluster to obtain a centroid.
4. Normalize the centroid.

The procedure described weights vectors both by their similarity to the pivot vector and by their invariance values with greatest weight being given to the invariance values.

The final basis of weighted data vectors should be used to determine a basis for the unweighted data vectors. When the r pivot vectors are used as a final basis for M, the corresponding unweighted vectors in the matrix of principal axes, P, of unweighted data vectors may be normalized and used as a basis for the unweighted data vectors. When this is done the final basis of unweighted data vectors will often be a simplest data basis. When there is more than one simplest data basis, the final basis so derived is the preferred basis.

When linear combinations of row vectors of M derived from clusters of vectors have been employed in obtaining the final basis of weighted vectors, the orthogonal transformation matrix carrying the weighted vectors of M to the unweighted vectors expressed in terms of the matrix of principal axes, P, (or of any other orthonormal basis vectors) has the form of Equation (4) with M and P replacing F

and F_1, respectively. The transformation matrix, X, is the $r \times r$ matrix of cosines with the unit principal axes of M being expressed as rows and the corresponding unit axes of P expressed as columns.

Assuming that the r vectors of the final weighted basis are expressed in the frame of the unit principal axes of M, denote the $r \times r$ matrix of inner products of unit basis vectors with the principal axes of M by $\overline{M}$. Then $\overline{M}X$ is an $r \times r$ matrix expressing the r basis vectors for the weighted unit data vectors of M as r rows in the frame of the principal axes of P. And $P(\overline{M}X)'$ gives the $nq \times r$ matrix of inner products of the unweighted data vectors on the basis of weighted data vectors. The matrix of cosines of the vectors of the basis is $\overline{MM}'$ since XX' is an identity matrix.

In general the vectors of the basis given by the rows of M are not a simplest data basis. Thus the $nq \times r$ matrix of coordinates of the unweighted data vectors on the vectors of the basis of weighted data vectors, given by $PX'\overline{M}'(\overline{MM}')^{-1}$, will contain negative elements and rotating to an orthogonal basis approximating the oblique basis will be required. Even though the matrix of coordinates is not in general non-negative, it is a preferred oblique basis for the unweighted data vectors because it is derived from those vectors having the highest invariance values. It therefore constitutes a good basis from which to obtain an approximating orthogonal basis to be used for hypothesis formation and inference.

The discussion of weighted data vectors and bases may be summarized as follows: Weighting data vectors and bases by normalizing data vectors and weighting by the inverse of the proportion of latent roots to the sum of the latent roots minimizes the role of the first principal axis in determining the reference frame. As such it minimizes that which is common to all of the behavior classified. The weighting process increases the cosines of unweighted boundary vectors already having relatively high cosines and decreases the cosines of unweighted boundary vectors already having low cosines. The vectors with high cosines with the first principal axis are, on the other hand, considerably shortened.

The principal axes of the matrix of inner products of the weighted data vectors emphasize what is common to the unweighted data vectors dissimilar to the first principal axis in a manner consistent with the dimensionality of the data space. They also yield measures of the stability or invariance of both single vectors and of the principal axes. The matrix, M, of coordinates of weighted data vectors on the principal axes may be regarded as the most nearly invariant matrix of coordinates for reasons quite analogous to the reasoning involved in the concept of factorial invariance in factor analysis. From M the r linearly independent most nearly invariant vectors or combinations of r groups of vectors may be used as r unit basis vectors and expressed as coordinates on the principal axes of the unweighted data vectors. When the r most nearly invariant vectors are used as a basis for the unweighted data vectors, the basis will either be a simplest data basis or one very similar to it. When clusters of weighted data vectors are used to form a basis for the unweighted data vectors, the basis will not be a simplest basis but again will be similar to a simplest basis. In this case, it is necessary to rotate to an orthogonal basis approximating the oblique basis.

In general bases formed from unweighted data vectors will not have maximal stability but will provide bases satisfactorily approximating the invariance of the principal axes of weighted data vectors. A distinctive advantage of M is that all vectors participate in its formation. A distinctive advantage of data bases is that the vectors of the basis are similar one by one to relatively widely spaced groups of vectors; thus the process of hypothesis formation is rendered less difficult.

TYPES AND TRAITS

The preceding discussion, being based upon the row vectors of the S matrix, that is, upon the sub-classes of behavior in a collection of responses, may be considered to be a discussion of traits. Following the lead of Thurstone (1947), a trait may be defined as a characteristic of an organism determined by what it does (in relation to what it does not do) in specified situations. On the other hand, types refer to kinds of organisms or subjects specified in terms of their traits. A typological study would then be equivalent to an analysis of the data matrix S by columns or an analysis of the row vectors of S', the transpose of S. The rank of S' will be the same as the rank of S. However, the matrix of coordinates on the basis vectors will, in the first case be $nq \times r$, whereas in the second case it will be $t \times r$, t being the number of subjects. It should be remembered that both traits and types inferred from classified behavior deserve only as much confidence as the classification system warrants. The warrant of confidence comes from the results of the data analysis which serves also as a basis for the definition of types and traits. When relationships of types or traits to variates external to the classification system have been found, an additional basis for confidence in the classification system has been established.

ANALYSIS OF THE DATA MATRIX S

Since only unit and zero entries are permitted in the data matrix, S, the row vector, designated as Y, with unit entries only is the longest possible vector. Whether or not it explicitly appears in S, it is a linear combination of the q rows corresponding to any response n_i. Since Y has t unit entries, the length of Y is $\sqrt{t}$ and the normalizing constant is $1/\sqrt{t}$. Normalizing all row vectors of S to Y and post-multiplying S by its transpose, gives

$$(1/\sqrt{t})\ SS'\ (1/\sqrt{t})\ =\ R_0 \tag{8}$$

with general element P_{ij} and diagonal element P_{ii}. The square symmetric matrix R_0 is thus a matrix of joint proportions. It should be noted that the diagonal entries of R_0 and the entries of $(1/t)\ SY'$ are identical.

It can be verified that

$$SY'\ =\ DZ' \tag{9}$$

and

$$SS'\ Z'\ =\ nDZ' \tag{10}$$

where D is the diagonal matrix formed from the diagonal entries only and Z' is a $1 \times nq$ matrix with unit entries only. Pre-multiplying (9) by D^{-1} gives

$$D^{-1}SS'\ Z'\ =\ nZ \tag{11}$$

which shows Z' to be a characteristic vector and n as a characteristic or latent root of $D^{-1}SS'$.

Pre-multiplying (11) by S' gives

$$(S'D^{-1}S)S'Z'\ =\ nS'Z' \tag{12}$$

but

$$S'Z'\ =\ nY' \tag{13}$$

Therefore

$$(S'D^{-1}S)\,Y'\ =\ nY' \tag{14}$$

showing n and Y' to be a characteristic root and a characteristic vector, respectively, of the symmetric matrix $(S'D^{-1}S)$. Furthermore, n must be the largest such root for the square matrices of (11) and (14) because under the one-and-zero coding system employed to obtain S, Y and Z' are the longest vectors in the row and column spaces implied by S. Pre-multiplying (11) by $D^{1/2}$ and inserting $D^{-1/2}D^{1/2}$ between S and Z' gives

$$(D^{-1/2}SS'D^{-1/2})D^{1/2}Z' = nD^{1/2}Z' \tag{15}$$

The matrix $D^{-1/2}SS'D^{-1/2}$, representing cosines of angles between the row vectors of S, is symmetric. Therefore, $D^{1/2}Z'$ is a characteristic vector of $D^{-1/2}SS'D^{-1/2}$ and n is the largest latent root. Furthermore, $(1/\sqrt{t})D^{1/2}Z'$ is the first principal axis for

$$[(1/\sqrt{t})ZD^{1/2}][(1/\sqrt{t})D^{1/2}Z'] = (1/t)(t_1 + t_2 + \ldots + t_{nq}) = n \tag{16}$$

and by definition the inner product of a principal axis vector with itself is the characteristic root associated with the characteristic vector. Post-multiplying the matrix of coordinates on the first principal axis, considered as a column matrix, by its transpose then gives an $nq \times nq$ square matrix which reduces $D^{-1/2}SS'D^{-1/2}$ maximally. The scalar element of $D^{-1/2}SS'D^{-1/2}$ is the formula for the product moment correlation for common elements. Analysis of S could be accomplished by taking the first principal axis of $D^{-1/2}SS'D^{-1/2}$ as the first basis vector; the second principal axis as the second basis vector, etc. However, the analysis will, instead, be based upon R_0. We note, therefore that the entries of $(1/t)SY'$, being entries of the first centroid of R_0, will usually be very similar to the corresponding entries of the first principal axis because obliqueness of data structure will usually obtain. The $nq \times nq$ matrix of unit rank $\{[(1/t)SY']\}$ $\{[(1/t)SY']'\}$ or equivalently, $(1/t)DZ'ZD(1/t)$, will then reduce R_0 effectively. This unit rank matrix has entries P_iP_j, the expression for the expectation of P_{ij}, the general element of R_0, when row vectors i and j are independent. The remainder matrix

$$R_1 = R_0 - (1/t)^2 DZ'ZD \tag{17}$$

has rank $r - 1$.

The greater an entry in $(1/t)SY'$, the longer the row vector of S corresponding to the entry. Hence the longer a row vector in S, the more it resembles Y and the less the angular separation between the two vectors.   Clearly then Y is, in a sense, in the "center" of the configuration of row vectors of S.   This fact and the fact that the inner products of the row vectors of S with Y are maximum inner products will be used in obtaining a final form for the analysis of S.

The remainder matrix discussed above will contain both positive and negative entries.   The negative entries correspond to the fact that each subject must "avoid" $q - 1$ sub-classes of the classification system in order to "select" one.   The positive entries show a joint tendency to "select."   Since the linear dependence in S due to Y has been removed, in the first remainder matrix R_1, the vectors denoted by the rows and columns of R_1 are independent of Y and are, in fact, orthogonal to Y.   Then another basis vector may be selected from R_1.   When normalized to the diagonal value, the entries treated as a column matrix and post-multiplied by its transpose, gives a second unit rank $nq \times nq$ matrix, which, when subtracted from R_1, results in a second remainder matrix, R_2.   Alternatively, a linear combination, such as the centroid vector of the first remainder matrix, may be used as a second basis vector.   In fact the whole collection of methods used in factor analysis may be applied to obtain a set of r basis vectors. Obtaining an $nq \times r$ matrix equivalent to S by employing successive remainder matrices is a routine matter depending only upon a choice of a single basis vector from each of the $R_1, R_2, \ldots, R_{r-1}$ remainder matrices.   However, the use of remainder matrices is cumbersome, the $nq \times r$ matrix of coordinates on basis vectors must then be transformed to the $nq \times r$ matrix corresponding to the simplest basis.   In general, obtaining successive remainder matrices to get $nq \times r$ matrices equivalent to S requires unnecessary labor.

For data matrices, S, which are $nq \times t$, as the number of basis vectors increases, the coordinates of the nq row vectors of S upon the basis vectors must in general decrease.   Consider for example, the long vector, Y.   It has unit length as represented in R_0 and, in general, cannot be a basis vector for a simple basis.   Then, as basis vectors are taken from R_0, the projections of Y must, on the average decrease; the scale changes as the number of basis vectors increases.   The scale can be held constant by normalizing the vectors defined upon a given basis vector by the coordinates of the row vectors of S to the vector defined upon the basis vector by coordinates of the long vector Y. Doing this for each basis vector gives a standard scale for interpreting projections no matter how many vectors in the basis.

In order to simplify the ensuing discussion, the following notations are used:

$$R_0 = (1/t)SS' \tag{18}$$

$$R_1 = R_0 - (1/t^2)DZ'ZD \tag{19}$$

Now $$R_0 = AR_aA' \tag{20}$$

where A is an $nq \times r$ matrix of parallel projections (coordinates) of row vectors of S upon the r simplest basis vectors and R_a is the $r \times r$ matrix of inner products of the simplest basis vectors. Also,

$$R_0 = VR_vV' \tag{21}$$

where V is the $nq \times r$ matrix defined by taking unique vectors orthogonal to all of the basis vectors represented in R_a but one. Matrix R_v is the matrix of inner products of those particular basis vectors which Thurstone calls reference factors. The relationship of the vectors expressed in R_a and R_v can be expressed as follows

$$R_a = DR_v^{-1}D \tag{22}$$

where D is the matrix of normalizing constants for the vectors whose self-inner products appear in the diagonals of R_v^{-1}. That each vector expressed in R_v is orthogonal to all but one of the vectors of R_a is shown below.

Let $$R_a = FF' \tag{23}$$

where F is a triangular matrix obtained by use of the Gramm-Schmidt orthogonalization process. In F the unit length basis vectors expressed in R_a in terms of their mutual inner products are now expressed as unit length row vectors. Since F is $r \times r$ and has rank r, it has an inverse and

$$FF^{-1} = I \tag{24}$$

also

$$FF^{-1}D = D \tag{25}$$

where D is the diagonal matrix of normalizing constants for the column vectors of F^{-1}. This is the same diagonal matrix as that of (22), also,

$$R_a^{-1} = F'^{-1}F^{-1} \tag{26}$$

and thus from (22) and (26) R_v is the normalized inverse of R_a and from (25) and (26) the column vectors of F^{-1} are just those vectors each of which is orthogonal to all vectors of the simple basis but one.

It should be noted that

$$R_0 = CR_cC' \qquad (27)$$

where C is an $nq \times r$ matrix of coordinates on an arbitrary basis. Thus any method of factoring a square symmetric matrix suffices to determine an $nq \times r$ matrix equivalent to R_0 which can be carried to an $nq \times r$ matrix, A, whose entries represent parallel projections on the vectors of a simple basis.

THE Q-TRANSFORMATION

Once R_0, A, and R_a have been determined, the inner product of the long vector, Y, with itself is given, when the rank is two, by

$$y_1^2 + y_2^2 + 2y_1y_2\phi_{12} \qquad (28)$$

where y_i are the coordinates of Y and ϕ_{12} is the cosine of the angle separating the two basis vectors. Equation (28) is extendable to the higher dimensional case. When rearranged as a symmetric matrix, Equation (28) shows in the diagonals the proportion of subjects in the class of subjects defined by each basis vector. The off-diagonal entries give the proportion of subjects common to both classes.

Now define the diagonal matrix Q with the entries being the coordinates of the vector Y on the basis vectors; that is, y_1 and y_2. Then

$$R_0 = (AQ^{-1})(QR_aQ)(Q^{-1}A') \qquad (29)$$

In Equation (29) QR_aQ is the matrix obtained by arranging the terms of Equation (28) as a symmetric matrix, the elements summing to unity. The entries in AQ^{-1} are the vectors, defined on the basis by the row vectors of S normalized to the projections of Y. Equation (29) introduces a standard scale of reference. If it is desired to use an orthogonal basis approximating the simplest basis, the Q-transformation should be applied to the matrix of inner products of the orthogonal basis vectors. Then Equation (29) becomes

$$R_0 = FQ^{-1}(QQ)Q^{-1}F' \qquad (30)$$

where QQ is a diagonal matrix because the basis is orthogonal and F is the $nq \times r$ matrix of coordinates on the orthogonal basis.

A particularly interesting case arises when the matrix of inner products of the vectors of the simplest basis is an identity matrix. Then Equation (30) is an expression of Equation (29) and the entries of FQ^{-1} may be interpreted as dependent probabilities whereas the entries of QQ may be thought of as independent probabilities, the probabilities referring to the probability of the class itself. However, such an interpretation seems not to be particularly useful for naturalistic investigation. In naturalistic investigation the hypotheses are embodied in the classification system. The questions of interest are:

1. How many classes exist; that is, what is the number of vectors in the basis?

2. What is the structure of the data?

3. Is the internal productivity sufficient to serve as a base for further hypothesis formation?

These questions are answered in terms of the index of internal productivity, in terms of the rank differential, and in terms of coordinates of data vectors. The problem is not to test hypotheses concerning the existence and number of a specified set of classes but, rather, from the observation of behavior and the analysis of data structure to find how many and what kinds of classes are implied by the data structure. In short, the aim is to produce more refined hypotheses, not to test hypotheses. To be sure certain hypotheses may be tested, but they are intrinsically rather trivial ones such as those connected with the number of basis vectors effectively exhausting the data of the S matrix.

ON THE USE OF COMMUNALITIES

The reduction of the matrix of joint proportions, R_0, to an $nq \times r$ matrix of coordinates on orthogonal basis vectors, with r taken as less than the actual rank R_0, may result in small negative inner products between the row vectors of the matrix. Negative inner products may be eliminated by the use of "communalities" analogous to the communalities of factor analysis. The use of communalities implies substitution of the original set of vectors by a new set. However, drastic as such a substitution may appear to be, the use of communalities has in fact the effect of altering the lengths of vectors and their angular separations while leaving the configuration of vectors essentially unaltered for purposes of inference and of hypothesis formation.

Consider

$$R_1 = R_0 - (1/t^2)SY'YS'$$

where R_1 is the first residual matrix after extraction of the first centroid axis. The first principal axis of R_0 is usually similar to the first centroid axis. Given an S matrix based on n responses and q alternatives, the $q \times q$ principal sub-matrices in R_0 corresponding to each of the n responses are diagonal with non-zero elements of P_i. In R_1 the corresponding $q \times q$ principal sub-matrices have diagonal entries $P_i(1 - P_i)$ with off-diagonal entries $-P_iP_j$. The sum of each row in the $q \times q$ principal sub-matrices of R_1 is zero.

A communality estimate for the diagonal values of R_1 may be obtained, as in factor analysis, by substituting the highest off-diagonal entry in the rows of R_1 for the diagonal entry excluding the $(q - 1)$ entries in the $q \times q$ principal sub-matrices corresponding to each response. The off-diagonal entries of the $(q \times q)$ principal sub-matrices are negative. Therefore it is desirable to increase these entries toward zero. The adjustment of all elements in a given $q \times q$ sub-matrix of R_1 corresponding to a given response may be accomplished by pre- and post-multiplication of the principal sub-matrix by the diagonal matrix W with elements

$$w_i = \frac{\sqrt{\|P_{ik} - P_iP_k\|}}{\sqrt{P_i(1 - P_i)}}$$

where i denotes the ith row of the $q \times q$ principal sub-matrix, $\|P_{ik} - P_iP_k\|$ is the absolute value of the highest off-diagonal element of the ith row and $P_i(1 - P_i)$ is the diagonal element. Such a pre- and post-multiplication of each $q \times q$ principal sub-matrix will result in a new $q \times q$ sub-matrix with $\|P_{ik} - P_iP_k\|$ in the diagonals and will move the negative off-diagonal entries toward zero. The new matrix may be designated by R_1^* and succeeding matrices R_2^*, etc. may be obtained in the same manner. There will be $(r - 1)$ of the R_1^* matrices, and $r - 1$ corresponding $nq \times 1$ matrices of coordinates on basis vectors determined from each. Denote the $nq \times (r - 1)$

matrix of coordinates by F, post-multiplying by F' and adding the $nq \times nq$ matrix of rank one, $(1/t^2)SY\,YS'$ gives

$$R_0^* = FF' + 1/t^2\, SY'YS'$$

where the elements not in the $q \times q$ principal sub-matrices corresponding to the responses are approximations to the elements of R_0. R_0^* and R_0 differ principally in the elements of the $q \times q$ principal sub-matrices corresponding to the responses. In R_0 these sub-matrices are diagonal, in R_0^* they are not necessarily so. Furthermore, the vector with elements P_i is a linear combination of the vectors of both R_0 and R_0^*. However, this vector is not necessarily the centroid of R_0^*; it is for R_0.

The matrix R_0, being the matrix of inner products of the vectors of the data vectors of the matrix S, which is a representation of behavior, refers directly to behavior. However, as is shown by the non-zero inner products in the $q \times q$ principal sub-matrices of R_0^* corresponding to the responses, R_0^* is not a matrix referring directly to behavior. Instead R_0^* may be taken as referring to response disposition or response tendencies which are not necessarily mutually exclusive whereas the responses classified are.

As in factor analysis, initial communality estimates may be unsatisfactory. However, again as in factor analysis, iteration to stable communalities should produce satisfactory results.

AN ILLUSTRATION WITH FICTITIOUS DATA

Table 2 is a matrix of inner products of the row vectors of S normalized to Y; that is, each vector is weighted by the constant, $1/\sqrt{t}$. So normalized to Y, the matrix of Table 2, R_0, is a symmetric matrix of joint proportions. The coordinates on the first two of the nine unit length principal axes are given in Table 3. The first two latent roots account for approximately 96% of the sum of the latent roots: two classes of behavior account for the great majority of the data. The best boundary vectors, those defining the simplest basis are those two data vectors having the highest positive and negative cosines with the second principal axis. These are the vectors numbered 1 and 13. The inner products of the remaining vectors with vectors 1 and 13, taken as unit length basis vectors, are given in Table 4.

TABLE 2*

DATA MATRIX OF INNER PRODUCTS, R_0.   (FICTITIOUS DATA OF TABLE 1)

	1	2	3	4	5	6	7	8	9	10	11	12	13	14	15	16
1	56	00	32	24	48	08	32	24	08	48	04	52	16	40	32	24
2		44	16	28	32	12	24	20	08	36	16	28	28	16	36	08
3			48	00	40	08	28	20	08	40	08	40	16	32	28	20
4				52	40	12	28	24	08	44	12	40	28	24	40	12
5					80	00	44	36	16	64	16	64	30	50	52	28
6						20	12	08	00	20	04	16	14	06	16	04
7							56	00	08	48	16	40	24	32	36	20
8								44	08	36	04	40	20	24	32	12
9									16	00	04	12	08	08	12	04
10										84	16	68	36	48	56	28
11											20	00	16	04	12	08
12												80	28	52	56	24
13													44	00	36	08
14														56	32	24
15															68	00
16																32

* Decimal points are omitted.

TABLE 3*

MATRIX P OF COORDINATES ON PRINCIPAL AXES OF R_0

	I	II
1	58	−34
2	42	39
3	48	−24
4	51	29
5	81	−10
6	18	14
7	56	01
8	44	04
9	14	02
10	85	02
11	18	18
12	82	−13
13	41	40
14	58	−35
15	69	29
16	31	−24

* Decimal points are omitted.

TABLE 4*

MATRIX A, INNER PRODUCTS OF ROW VECTORS OF TABLE 3 ON THE VECTORS OF THE OBLIQUE SIMPLEST BASIS

	A_1	A_2
1	66	18
2	16	57
3	54	17
4	30	57
5	74	51
6	08	23
7	48	40
8	36	35
9	12	12
10	72	63
11	06	25
12	78	50
13	15	57
14	67	17
15	45	69
16	39	06
Y	84	75

* Decimal points are omitted.

TABLE 5*

MATRIX, R_a, OF INNER PRODUCTS
OF VECTORS OF THE OBLIQUE
SIMPLEST BASIS R_a

	A_1	A_2
A_1	100	27
A_2	27	100

* Decimal points are omitted.

Table 5 shows the matrix of the inner products, R_a, between the vectors of the simplest basis, the vectors being taken at unit length. The index of internal productivity,

TABLE 6*

MATRIX, F, OF COORDINATES ON
ORTHOGONAL BASIS APPROXIMATING
THE OBLIQUE SIMPLEST BASIS

	I	II
1	66	09
2	09	56
3	53	10
4	23	55
5	69	42
6	05	23
7	43	34
8	32	31
9	11	11
10	66	54
11	02	25
12	73	40
13	08	57
14	67	08
15	37	64
16	39	00
Y	76	65

* Decimal points are omitted.

TABLE 7*

MATRIX FQ^{-1}

	I	II
1	89	14
2	12	86
3	71	15
4	29	85
5	93	65
6	07	35
7	58	52
8	42	48
9	15	17
10	85	83
11	03	38
12	97	62
13	11	88
14	89	12
15	50	99
16	50	01

* Decimal points are omitted.

computed from the data of Table 5, is .73, indicating considerable internal productivity for the fictitious classification system.

Table 6 gives the matrix, F, of coordinates on the vectors of an orthogonal basis approximating the oblique simplest basis vectors and Table 7 gives the results of applying the Q-transformation. Table 8 shows the proportion of subjects in

TABLE 8*

MATRIX QQ OF CLASS PROPORTIONS

58	
	42

* Decimal points are omitted.

each class.   Communalities were not used in these computations.

It is from matrices such as those of Table 7 and 8 that the interpretation of the classes of behavior should be made.   The interpretation is, in fact, a reformulation and extension of the hypotheses embodied in the classification system.

SUMMARY

The classified behavior of subjects may be represented in the form of a data matrix, S, which, when analyzed in terms of internal productivity, leads to an extension or reformulation of original hypotheses as represented in the classification system used.   The original classes of behavior as represented in the data matrix, S, may be replaced by at most $nq - n + 1$ behavior classes, the vectorial representations of which serve as a basis for the data vectors of S.

For a given S matrix with rank r there will be many bases for S. A fundamental problem is that of selecting the most appropriate basis for purposes of inference and hypothesis formation.   The most appropriate *data* basis is the simplest basis consisting of r best boundary vectors.   The boundary vectors are those vectors generating non-negative matrices of coordinates and the best boundary vectors are among those at most $2(r - 1)$ data vectors having the highest cosines with the principal axes starting with the second and the data vector with the lowest cosine with the first principal axis.   The simplest basis is the most appropriate basis because it is the data basis for which the matrix of coordinates of the data vectors is expected to vary the least under repeated sampling or under changes in the classification system.

An alternative, and perhaps better, basis than the simplest basis is the basis of principal axes of the weighted data vectors.   The data vectors of S are weighted by expressing the data vectors in terms of coordinates on principal axes and weighting the coordinates on the kth principal axis inversely as the proportions p_k/p where p_k is the kth latent root and p is the sum of the latent roots.   This weighting relatively lengthens the boundary vectors and relatively shortens those vectors largely accounted for by the principal axes with the larger latent roots.   Since the vectors of the basis are determined by all of the weighted vectors, but largely by the boundary vectors, it is expected that the matrix of coordinates on the vectors of the weighted basis will vary less from sample to sample than the coordinates of the simplest basis.

Instead of using the matrix of coordinates on the principal axes of the weighted data vectors, one may use a basis of r weighted data vectors.

If it is desired to use a basis for the unweighted data vectors represented in P (p. 39), the r vectors of P with the same numbers as the r pivot vectors of M may be selected as basis vectors. Or the r pivot vectors or the vectors of the basis derived from clusters of vectors in M may be expressed with their coordinates on the principal axes of matrix P and used as the basis for the unweighted data vectors. The application of the Q-transformation will then put all coordinates on a standard scale. It is the Q-transformed matrix of coordinates which should be used as the beginning point for hypothesis formation and inference. When a basis of weighted data vectors is used, the Q-transformation should not be employed.

CHAPTER THREE

VARIATIONS ON THE S MATRIX AND WEIGHTS FOR SUBJECTS

FORMING S FROM DATA MATRICES NOT IN STANDARD FORM

In exploratory analysis the matrix S is said to be in standard form because, given a unit of response and a classification system, S represents a description of behavior. Other representations of behavior could be used. For example an "answer pattern" may be represented as a vector with one unit entry, all remaining entries being zero. Then the answer patterns all have inner products of zero or unity when the vectors have been normalized. Such a procedure may be logically impeccable but in fact involves arbitrary operations upon the vectors represented by the column vectors of S, for the information represented in each column of S must be known before the vectors with but one non-zero entry representing each answer pattern can be constructed. Thus S or some array of data logically equivalent to S is logically prior to such a matrix representing answer patterns. What is of importance here is that representations of behavior which seem to be equivalent and to contain exactly the same information as S do not in fact do so.

We turn now to a more subtle problem of equivalence, that in which different aspects of each of a set of responses are classified. It is not always realized that classifying aspects of a response may introduce dependence which must be taken into account. A schematic data matrix, in which aspects of each response have been classified, is shown in Table 9. Each unit of behavior has been classified on the basis of two aspects called X and Z. In X, each response is classified into one of two sub-classes denoted by A and B. In Z, each unit is further classified into two categories, D and E. At first glance, the

TABLE 9

FICTITIOUS DATA MATRIX

Responses $n = 3$	Main Aspects of Responses	Sub-Aspects of Responses	Subjects 1 2 3 4 5 6 7 8 9 10 11 12
1	X	A	1 0 1 0 0 1 0 1 0 0 0 1
	X	B	0 1 0 1 1 0 1 0 1 1 1 0
	Z	D	0 1 1 0 0 0 0 1 1 1 0 1
	Z	E	1 0 0 1 1 1 1 0 0 0 1 0
2	X	A	0 0 1 1 1 0 1 0 1 0 1 0
	X	B	1 1 0 0 0 1 0 1 0 1 0 1
	Z	D	0 0 0 1 1 0 1 0 1 0 1 0
	Z	E	1 1 1 0 0 1 0 1 0 1 0 1
3	X	A	1 0 1 0 0 1 1 1 1 0 0 0
	X	B	0 1 0 1 1 0 0 0 0 1 1 1
	Z	D	1 1 0 0 1 0 0 0 0 1 1 1
	Z	E	0 0 1 1 0 1 1 1 1 0 0 0

matrix of Table 9 seems to be an appropriate matrix for analysis for it shows just what each subject did and did not do and thus seems to be equivalent to S, which contains just one unit entry for each response. However, when this matrix is compared with its apparently equivalent S matrix the problem of introduced dependence becomes apparent.

Consider first the maximum rank of the matrix of Table 9. The row vector, Y, of maximum length is the sum of the two rows of each of the six 2×12 submatrices corresponding to the three responses. Thus, the vector Y occurs twice for each response, six times in all. It follows that the rank is at most 7.

Now consider Table 10. It contains a data matrix derived from the same data that is recorded in Table 9 by forming new mutually exclusive classes from the combinations of the sub-classes of X and Z. Thus, a unit classified as A may also be classified D or E. Therefore,

TABLE 10

FICTITIOUS DATA IN STANDARD FORM, S

Responses $n = 3$	Classes $q = 4$	Subjects											
		1	2	3	4	5	6	7	8	9	10	11	12
1	A,D	0	0	1	0	0	0	0	1	0	0	0	1
	A,E	1	0	0	0	0	1	0	0	0	0	0	0
	B,D	0	1	0	0	0	0	0	0	1	1	0	0
	B,E	0	0	0	1	1	0	1	0	0	0	1	0
2	A,D	0	0	0	1	1	0	1	0	1	0	1	0
	A,E	0	0	1	0	0	0	0	0	0	0	0	0
	B,D	0	0	0	0	0	0	0	0	0	0	0	0
	B,E	1	1	0	0	0	1	0	1	0	1	0	1
3	A,D	1	0	0	0	0	0	0	0	0	0	0	0
	A,E	0	0	1	0	0	1	1	1	1	0	0	0
	B,D	0	1	0	0	1	0	0	0	0	1	1	1
	B,E	0	0	0	1	0	0	0	0	0	0	0	0

the classes (A, D) or (A, E) are possible. Similarly a unit classified as B may also be classified as D or E, so the classes (B, D) or (B, E) are also possible. Then we have, for each response, four mutually exclusive sub-classes. Since, n, the number of responses, is 3, the data matrix, as before, contains nq rows. Now, however, the vector Y occurs but three times, once for each response rather than twice for each response. Hence the maximal possible rank for exactly the same behaviors as those in Table 9 is 10. Thus there is more dependence in Table 9 than in Table 10. It follows that the vector space associated with the first matrix is a sub-space of that associated with the second, for although both are based on the same classification of the same responses, the rank of the second is greater than that of the first. Elementary row operations will transform the rows of the first matrix into those of the second. But the rows of the second cannot be transformed into those of the first. It seems, therefore, that the form of the second matrix is more fundamental than that of the first.

Every set of classifications may be brought to the standard form and problems of dependence which may be introduced by variations from the standard form can thus be avoided. The basic procedure is simple. S can be formed by requiring that for each response with q alternatives of response, there be one and only one unit entry, the remainder being zero entries.

MATRICES DERIVED FROM S BY HYPOTHESIS

Once the data is in the standard form of S the investigator might have hypotheses which imply a matrix which embodies the hypotheses rather than the data itself. For example, the investigator might have the notion that thirds of interviews constitute a basic sequence, more basic than the sequence of responses. When this is the case, S may be changed in accordance with the hypothesis.

Let g be the number of collections of responses the investigator desires to keep in sequence; the within-collection responses not to be kept in sequence. Then define the matrix S_c such that for each of the collections of responses there are $nq/g = n_c$ rows. S, from which S_c is derived, has nq rows and S_c has gn_c rows with $gn_c = nq$. One such matrix, S_c, derived from an S matrix with $n = 6$, $q = 3$, is shown schematically in Table 11.

In S_c of Table 11 the sequence of responses has been dichotomized. Therefore, the unit entries do not have the same meaning as those in the matrix S from which they were derived. The first two unit entries in the first row indicate that one response classified as a occurred in the first half of the sequence of responses for each of the first two subjects. Within the first half, however, each response may have occurred at any point in the sequence. The three unit entries in the second column of S_c indicate that three of the type a responses occurred in the first half of the total sequence for the second subject. Note that these three responses are in sequence. The first unit entry codes the first a-type response, etc. Thus, for S_c, complete similarity of behavior as indicated by inner products of 6 between column vectors can occur when in the S matrix from which S_c was derived, the inner products of the column vectors may all be zero.

Matrix S_c is of order $gn_c \times t$, where t is the number of subjects. That the maximal possible rank for a given S_c is, as in the analysis of S, $gn_c - (gn_c/q) + 1$ is shown directly by the fact that the row vector Y with unit entries only may occur n/g times in each of the g_i. The maximal possible rank of S_c in Table 11 with $t > nq$ is 13.

Given the information that the q categories of the classification system are mutually exclusive, we know at once that S_c was derived from a matrix S for which $nq - n + 1 = 13$. For there are $nq = gn_c$ rows and q mutually exclusive classes. However, S_c cannot be derived from S by elementary row or column operations. Therefore,

TABLE 11

DATA MATRIX, S_c

$g = 2$	$q = 3$	$n_c = 9$	Subjects		
			1	2 . . . . . . t	
	a	1	1	1	
		2	0	1	
		3	0	1	
g_1	b	1	1	0	
		2	0	0	
		3	0	0	
	c	1	1	0	
		2	0	0	
		3	0	0	
	a	4	1	1	
		5	1	0	
		6	1	0	
g_2	b	4	0	1	
		5	0	0	
		6	0	0	
	c	4	0	1	
		5	0	0	
		6	0	0	

S_c corresponds to a different universe of discourse than S, occasioned by neglecting consideration of the actual sequence of responses on the basis of hypothesis or of prior knowledge. S_c is particularly useful for assessing similarity between columns and may be analyzed in the same manner as S'. Caution should be exercised in analyzing the rows of S_c, for the meaning of the row vectors can, in specific cases, be quite ambiguous. One way to keep in mind the potential loss of information resulting from the use of matrices of the type S_c is to realize that a given S_c matrix can be derived from different S matrices and that different S_c matrices can be derived from the same S matrix. On the other hand since each S_c matrix derived from a given S matrix represents an hypothesis or set of hypotheses about the behavior represented in S, the analysis of S_c matrices can be very illuminating. An actual S_c matrix is analyzed in Chapter VI.

WEIGHTS FOR SUBJECTS

Other types of problems than those considered here may be analyzed by bringing data into the standard form of the S matrix. For example, suppose there are q objects to which t subjects respond on n occasions in such a way that it can be ascertained that one of them is preferred over the remaining $q - 1$ on occasion n_i. Then assigning a unit score to the preferred object and zero scores to the non-preferred objects generates an $nq \times t$ matrix, S, showing which objects were most preferred on which occasion. S can then be analyzed for the structural relations underlying the observed first preferences.

Sometimes one may wish to consider all of the preferences of t subjects over p objects for q categories of discrimination and for n occasions. For this purpose a $q \times p$ matrix may be constructed for each subject for one occasion which contains p unit elements and $p(q - 1)$ zero elements. The complete matrix over all subjects and occasions will be $nq \times pt$. The n different $q \times pt$ submatrices may be summed to get a summary matrix of frequencies. The summary matrix is often the matrix of choice when one desires to use a least squares approach to scaling.

In least squares scaling one is interested in finding a set of "weights" for categories or of "scores" for subjects which best discriminate in the sense of least squares. The scales are derived from the internal consistency of the data of S or from matrices derived from S, not from matrices of underlying structural relations. The least squares scales are transformations of successive latent vectors adjusted to zero mean and unit variance for the data of S. Since a set of "optimal" or least squares scales for a particular set of data is derived from successive latent vectors, they emphasize what is common to the sub-categories in $r, r - 1, r - 2, \ldots, r - r + 1$ dimensions.

In exploratory analysis the case is quite different from that of least squares scaling; although one might start with exactly the same data in both cases. In exploratory analysis the simplest basis (or an orthogonal basis best approximating the simplest basis) is derived from behavior vectors as different as possible for the configuration of behavior vectors at hand. In other words the best discriminating vectors are defined as those which best reflect differences in actual behavior; thus "discrimination" here has an empirical or naturalistic tinge. Those vectors of S defining a simplest basis are those with the smallest cosines with each other. The problem of weighting the actual behavior as represented in S *then becomes one of weighting it in terms of its relevance to underlying vectors,* the underlying vectors being projections of the vectors of S into an r-dimensional sub-space.

Weighting the actual behavior of the subjects can be accomplished as follows. Denote by D_j the diagonal matrix formed from the jth column of the final $(nq \times r)$ matrix of coordinates on basis vectors before the Q transformation has been applied. The Y row should be excluded. Then find D_jS and transform the entries in D_jS in such a way that their mean becomes zero and their sum of squares is unity. Denote this matrix by $\overline{S_j}$. Then find $Z\overline{S_j}$ where Z has unit entries and is $1 \times nq$. This is the array of scores for each subject for the jth basis vector. The more similar the scores the more similar the subjects are in terms of the underlying response dispositions. The entries of $\overline{S_j}$ are the weights assigned to each category for each response and the score of each subject is the mean of his subcategory weights. Each subject gets r scores for there are r matrices of the type S_j, one for each basis vector.

It should be remembered that the scores for the individuals are the sums of n of the weights assigned to the q_i by the operations described and it should be emphasized that the scores for the individuals are not "factor" scores. They represent the weighting of behavior based on ascertained underlying relations.

In some cases the investigator may wish on the basis of hypothesis or of prior knowledge to assign weights to the rows of S which are different from those assigned by the basis vectors. These weights should then be written as a diagonal matrix and post-multiplied into the $(nq + 1) \times r$ matrix of coordinates on unit basis vectors after which the Q transformation should be applied. The weight given to the Y row should be equal to or greater than any other. Then the S matrix may be treated as before. In our opinion the application of arbitrary or hypothetical weights is not a matter of internal analysis but rather of external analysis. The relationship with criteria or the differential relationship of hypothetical and derived weights with criteria is what counts. Above all, the analysis of the arbitrary or hypothetical weights is not a matter of purely statistical analysis. Finally, we believe that hypotheses should be introduced into the data only in the sense that the sequence of responses is condensed or changed as when in interviews, for example, thirds or halves of interviews are taken as the unit of analysis rather than the response.

CHAPTER FOUR

ORTHOGONAL BASES
APPROXIMATING AN OBLIQUE
SIMPLEST BASIS

In an exploratory analysis the matrix of inner products of the vectors of the simplest basis, R_a, is the matrix which defines the internal productivity of the classification system. As such it is fundamental. However, in general R_a will not be an identity matrix, reflecting the fact that most empirical categories will not be mutually exclusive. Oblique bases confront us with essential and mathematical difficulties, the essential difficulty being that overlapping categories present complex problems of inference. Since R_a will usually be respectably close to being orthogonal, an orthogonal basis approximating the oblique basis represented in R_a will have associated with it an $nq \times r$ matrix of inner products of the vectors of S with the orthogonal basis vectors which will be very similar to A, the $nq \times r$ matrix of coordinates of the vectors of S in the basis represented in R_a.

There are several possibilities to consider in deciding how to approximate the oblique simple basis with an orthogonal basis. One possibility is simply to use graphical rotation and eyesight; graphical rotation is a good candidate for being a preferred method when the configuration of vectors is such that a good approximating position is obvious. This will often be the case. In considering computational methods we observe, following Green (1952), that the problem is to find the $nq \times r$ matrix, G, where

$$A\Lambda = G \tag{33}$$

where G is the matrix of coordinates associated with the best fitting orthogonal basis and Λ is an orthogonal transformation matrix with vectors of unit length. In general no such Λ exists. Therefore, there is no orthogonal basis best fitting A in any absolute sense and a criterion for defining G is needed; the criterion may be objective but the selection of a given criterion is not an objective process.

One type of criterion for selecting a best fitting orthogonal basis is a least-squares criterion. Unfortunately, several least-squares criteria can be used which give different "best-fitting" orthogonal bases. One can take a least-squares fit to R_v, the reference basis to R_a, or a least-squares fit to R_a can be used. Furthermore, one can use least-squares fits to the $nq \times r$ matrices of coordinates associated with R_a and R_v. There seems to be no compelling reason for preferring any one of the least-squares solutions. One sensible solution is that which depends upon R_a for it is the basis which most directly defines internal productivity. Green has considered this case among others. What follows depends upon his development. By reference to his paper (1952) it can be shown that

$$\Lambda = (A'GG'A)^{-1/2}A'G \tag{34}$$

where the fractional exponent is defined as follows: $Y = X^{1/2}$ if and only if $Y^2 = X$; by $X^{-1/2}$ is meant Y^{-1}. For any $n \times n$ square symmetrix matrix of rank n such as $(A'GG'A)$ one can find an orthogonal matrix P such that

$$A'GG'A = PDP' \tag{35}$$

where the columns of P are the latent vectors of $A'GG'A$ and the elements in the diagonal matrix D are the corresponding latent roots. Now from (35) we have

$$(A'GG'A)^{1/2} = PD^{1/2}P' \tag{36}$$

for

$$PD^{1/2}P'PD^{1/2}P' = PDP'$$

because P is an orthogonal matrix for which $P'P$ is an I matrix. Therefore,

$$(A'GG'A)^{-1/2} = PD^{-1/2}p' \tag{37}$$

The orthogonal transformation matrix, Λ, may be obtained by determining the latent vectors and latent roots of $A'GG'A$. These vectors and roots are then arranged as the matrices P and D. Finally $D^{-1/2}$ is simply the matrix of reciprocals of the positive square roots of D.

Λ is then found by using equations (34) and (37). Applying the method to R_a we find

$$\Lambda = (FF')^{-1/2}F' \tag{38}$$

where F is obtained from R_a by the diagonal method of factoring. This is equivalent to maximizing the sum of the cosines of the angles between the simple axes and the corresponding orthogonal axes. Since cosines are a measure of similarity, maximizing the sum of the cosines maximizes similarity.

Since the kinds of least-squares fits are many, the computations lengthy, and the choice personal, we outline below a method for finding an orthogonal basis which is simultaneously a best fit to R_a and to R_v in the sense of a minimum sum of differences of cosines. The method may be considered as an extension of Gibson's (1952). Given R_a, the problem is to find an orthogonal basis whose vectors have minimally different angles with the corresponding vectors of R_a and R_v. Finding a basis with minimally different angles is not difficult: simply bisect the angles between the corresponding vectors of R_a and of R_v. However, this basis, found by taking centroids, is not in general an orthogonal basis. But it is clearly closer to orthogonality than the bases of R_a and of R_v for if the inner products of R_a are positive, then those of R_v will be, or tend to be, negative. We will now look more closely at this fact. Consider

$$R_a = FF' \tag{39}$$

where F is obtained by the diagonal method of factoring with unity in the diagonals and

$$FF^{-1} = I \tag{40}$$

$$FF^{-1}L = L \tag{41}$$

where L is the matrix of normalizing constants for the columns of F^{-1}. Also consider

$$F' + F^{-1}L \tag{42}$$

and

$$M(F' + F^{-1}L)'(F' + F^{-1}L)M \equiv R_1 \tag{43}$$

where M is a diagonal matrix of normalizing constants for the columns of $F' + F^{-1}L$. The claim is that the sequence of matrices

$$R_a, R_1, R_2, \ldots, R_n \tag{44}$$

goes to I, the identity matrix.

In (40) the sum of squares of each row of F is unity with the first diagonal value being unity and the others equal to or less than unity. This is a consequence of the diagonal method. If (40) is to hold, the sum of squares of each column of F^{-1} must be greater than unity when the diagonal values of F are not unity. Since the rows of F represent unit length vectors and the columns of F^{-1} do not, the I matrix of (40) represents the perpendicular projections of non-normalized vectors upon normalized vectors. Thus the I matrix of (40) shows that the vectors of the columns of F^{-1} have zero inner products with all of the unit basis vectors save one. This implies that the angular separation of the vectors represented by the columns of F^{-1} are greater than those represented by the rows of F and thus of R_a. More precisely, the sum of the cosines of the angles between the vectors of R_a is greater than the sum of the cosines between the column vectors of F^{-1}. Equation (41) shows the effects on (40) of normalizing the columns of F^{-1} and shows that the normalizing constants are the cosines of the angles between the simple vectors and the reference vectors of $F^{-1}L$. Equation (41) justifies the use of the expression, reference vector, (used in Thurstone's sense) because it shows that the normalized column vectors of F^{-1} are each perpendicular to all but one of the simple vectors.

Equation (42) is an expression for vector sums. Consider the columns: by the parallelogram law, the vectors of (42) are in the planes spanned by the non-orthogonal (associated) simple and reference vectors. It follows that the sum of the cosines between the column vectors of $F' + F^{-1}L$ is less than the sum of the cosines in R_a and more than the sum of the cosines in R_v, the matrix of inner products of the reference vectors. Furthermore, R_2 will be more orthogonal than R_1 because R_2 is obtained from R_1 in the same way that R_1 is obtained from R_a.

Although the sum of the cosines in the off-diagonal entries of R_1, $R_2, \ldots, R_n$ becomes successively less, there remains the question of whether the sums of the cosines of R_1, say, can be less than zero. The question can be answered in the negative because the diagonal values of the inverses of the F_i have minimum values of unity since the diagonal values of the F_i have maximum values of unity. Equation (40) guarantees that when the diagonals of F^{-1} are unity then so are the diagonals of F. Since the sum of squares of each row of F is

unity, F then becomes an I matrix and $F = F' = R = R^{-1}$. Therefore, the sum of the cosines of each of the R_i is equal to or greater
than zero.

Another question arises: Even though the sum of the cosines of
the matrices R_a, R_1, . . ., R_n becomes less and less, does it happen that
the sequence goes to I? The answer is in the affirmative. For,
consider the sequence

$$F' + F^{-1}, F_1' + F_1^{-1}, \ldots, F_n' + F_n^{-1} \tag{45}$$

The ith diagonal value of F, for example x, is equal to or less than
unity; of F^{-1} is $1/x$, of $F' + F^{-1}$ is $x + 1/x$. Also the ith diagonal
value of $F_1' + F_1^{-1}$ is $x_1 + 1/x_1$. However, $x_1 > x$. Hence we have
the sequence

$$x + 1/x > x_1 + 1/x_1 > \ldots > x_n + 1/x_n \tag{46}$$

The maximum value of x_i is unity and the minimum value of $1/x_i$ is
unity. This minimum is, of course, reached when x_i is unity and
the minimum value of $x_i + 1/x_i$ is 2. It can be shown that the sequence (46) converges; as a consequence (45) converges. Now save
possibly for the first diagonal value of $F_1' + F_1^{-1}$ values of 2 in the
diagonal can occur only when the off-diagonal entries of the columns
are zero. Hence $r - 1$ of the vectors of $(F_1' + F_1^{-1})$ are orthogonal
when the diagonal values are 2 and the value 2 can be attained, for the
sequence converges. Now if the off-diagonal column entries of
$(F_i' + F_i^{-1})$ are zero, so are the off-diagonal row entries. Therefore,
if the diagonal values of $(F_i' + F_i^{-1})$ are 2, the column vectors of
$(F_i' + F_i^{-1})$ must be orthogonal.

The same results will be obtained if one starts the orthogonalization process with R_v the matrix of the reference basis instead of R_a.

The process of computing represents in effect successive bisections
of angles, each set of bisections being determined by the previous one.
Bisection certainly minimizes the differences between the angles
created by the bisection. The final orthogonal basis, therefore, is
obtained by a series of minimizing processes. The presumption is
that what is minimized is the sum of differences of the cosines of the
final orthogonal basis on the one hand and the vectors of the simple
basis and the associated vectors of the reference basis on the other.
A detailed proof that (44) goes to I is given in Appendix B.

The process of orthogonalizing is shown in Table 12. The steps in the computational process follow:

1. Given R_a, the matrix of inner products of vectors of the simple basis, find F by the diagonal method of factoring.

2. Compute F^{-1}. Since F is triangular with zero entries above the main diagonal, it is convenient to use the relation $F'F'^{-1} = I$ for computing F^{-1}. F'^{-1} has as diagonal entries the reciprocals of the diagonal entries of F'. The entries of F'^{-1} below the main diagonal are zero so only the entries above the main diagonal are unknown. Since the inner products of the row vectors of F' and the column vectors of F'^{-1} are zero, the unknown value in F'^{-1} may always be solved for with but one unknown if one starts by solving for the unknown entries of F'^{-1}, working up from the main diagonal in each column. Note that $F'^{-1} = (F^{-1})'$.

3. Normalize the columns of F^{-1} with the diagonal matrix L. The jth entry of L is $1/\sqrt{l_j}$ where l_j is the sum of squares of the jth column of F^{-1}.

4. Take $(F' + F^{-1}L)M$ where M is a diagonal matrix whose entries are $1/\sqrt{m_j}$ where m_j is the sum of squares of the jth column of $(F' + F^{-1}L)$ and premultiply by its transpose. The result is

$$M(R_a + LR_a^{-1}L + 2L)M = R_1 \qquad (47)$$

Equation (47) is the matrix of inner products of the approximate orthogonal basis. If R_1 does not sufficiently approximate orthogonality it may be treated as though it were R_a and the process repeated to get R_2. R_1 will often be a satisfactory approximation to orthogonality. R_2 will nearly always be a satisfactory approximation to orthogonality.

5. Find

$$AF(F' + F^{-1}L)M = A(R_aM + LM)$$
$$= \bar{A}(M + R_a^{-1}LM) \qquad (48)$$

where A is the matrix of coordinates on the simplest basis and $\bar{A}$ is the matrix of inner products of the data vectors with the vectors of the simplest basis. This is the transformation carrying A or $\bar{A}$ to the best-fitting orthogonal basis when R_1 is orthogonal or considered to be satisfactorily orthogonal. When R_1 is not satisfactorily orthogonal, R_2 must be found. Associated with R_2 is $(F_1' + F_1^{-1}L_1)M_1$. If R_2 is satisfactory, then the transformation carrying A to the best fitting orthogonal basis is

$$A(R_aM + LM)(M_1 + R_1^{-1}L_1M_1) \qquad (49)$$

It should be noted that in (48) F is introduced to get the vectors of A expressed in the same arbitrary orthogonal frame as the vectors of R_a and R_v which are in $F + F'^{-1}$ respectively.

When the off-diagonal entries of R_a are equal, then the off-diagonal entries of $LR_a^{-1}L$ will also be equal and opposite in sign to those of R_a. When the R_a is of rank 2,

then $\qquad\qquad R_a + LR_a^{-1}L = \text{diagonal } (2, 2, \ldots, 2) \qquad (50)$

In this case the values of

$$R_a + LR_a^{-1}L + 2L = \text{diagonal}$$
$$(2 + 2l_1,\ 2 + 2l_2,\ \ldots,\ 2 + 2l_r) \qquad (51)$$

But the values of M are $m_i = 1/\sqrt{2 + 2l_i}$. Thus the orthogonalization process yields an orthogonal basis in one step when the rank of R_a is 2. When the rank is greater than 2, with all off-diagonal entries of R_a being equal, convergence to an I matrix depends on the values of the l_i. It is to be expected that the more similar the entries of R_a and the smaller they are the more rapid the convergence to I. The symmetry is most important, for widely varying values in R_a give rise to a process in which the variation is smoothed much as in averaging.

It is interesting to note that two of Green's least-squares solutions are identical when the elements of L are identical. The solutions referred to are, respectively, those in which the best orthogonal approximations to reference vectors and to the vectors of the original oblique basis are sought. The values of L will always be identical when the rank is 2. Hence Green's solution and our solution are identical when the rank is 2. Now Green's solutions simultaneously maximize the sum of the cosines between the corresponding orthogonal and reference axes and the corresponding orthogonal and simple axes when the values of L are equal. This is the same as minimizing the sum of the differences between the angles between the orthogonal and reference axes and the orthogonal and simple axes respectively. Thus when the l_i are equal, our solution and Green's two solutions based on primary axes and reference axes will be identical. As the l_i vary, Green's bases will "rotate away" from each other. In practice

TABLE 12

ORTHOGONALIZATION COMPUTING METHOD
FOR DATA OF TABLE 4

	R_a			$R_a^{-1}LM$			$\bar{A}(M + R_a^{-1}LM)$	
	A_1	A_2		.52	$-.14$		I	II
A_1	1.00	.27		$-.14$	.52	1	.66	.09
A_2	.27	1.00				2	.09	.56
						3	.53	.10
				$LR_a^{-1}L = R_v$		4	.23	.55
	F			1.00	$-.27$	5	.69	.42
	I	II		$-.27$	1.00	6	.05	.23
A	1.00	0				7	.43	.34
B	.27	.96				8	.32	.31
						9	.11	.11
				$R_a + R_v + 2L$		10	.66	.54
	F'^{-1}			3.93	00	11	.02	.25
	1.00	$-.28$		00	3.93	12	.73	.40
	00	1.04				13	.08	.57
						14	.67	.08
				$M(R_a + R_v + 2L)M$		15	.37	.64
	R_a^{-1}			.98	00	16	.39	.00
	1.08	$-.29$		00	.98	Y	.76	.65
	$-.29$	1.08						
				$(M + R_a^{-1}LM)$				
	L			1.03	$-.14$			
	.96			$-.14$	1.03			
		.96						
	M							
	.50							
		.50						
	LM							
	.49							
		.49						

therefore, our solution will generally closely resemble Green's two solutions for, as he points out, his solutions will yield very similar results in most cases. To put the matter another way, taking the centroids of his solutions should yield a set of basis vectors very similar to those attained by our solutions.

The computations using the orthogonalization method are shown in Table 12, for the data of Table 1, Chapter II and from Tables 4 and 5.

Matrix R_a of Table 12 is identical with the matrix of Table 5. F was obtained from R_a by the diagonal method of factoring and F'^{-1} was obtained from the relation $F'F'^{-1} = I$. L is the diagonal matrix of normalizing constants for the rows of F'^{-1} and for R_a^{-1}. The entries of M are $m_i = 1/\sqrt{2 + 2l_i}$ where l_i is the diagonal entry of the ith row of L. The rest of the table is self-explanatory.

It should be remembered that the orthogonalization process illustrated applies to any set of oblique basis vectors. Thus, one may estimate R_a from R_0, orthogonalize and rotate graphically to R_a if the estimated R_a is not the actual R_a. Orthogonalizing on the actual R_a then gives the final approximating orthogonal basis.

CHAPTER FIVE

HIGHER ORDER MATRICES
AND VECTORS

The basic data matrix S in standard form is a representation of behavior in terms of the classification system applied to a set of responses as they occur. The rows and columns of S enjoy a unique status: They are the original, empirically given, vectors. Other vectors cannot be constructed without possession of the information contained in S. Of particular interest are what might be called the higher order vectors. As the row vectors of S show the single occurrences and generate the pairs of occurrences, so do vectors exist which generate the triples, quadruples, etc., of occurrences. The vectors showing the pairs and generating the triples of occurrences may be constructed as follows: consider row vectors i and j of S, i corresponding to n_i and j corresponding to n_j. Form a new vector denoted by $i\&j$, the elements of which are the products of correspondingly placed elements in row vectors i and j. The vector $i\&j$ is a Boolean "and" vector showing directly the responses common to vectors i and j in S. In matrix notation the different vectors of the form $i\&j$ may be written $S\&i$. $S\&i$ is an $nq \times t$ matrix representing the Boolean "and" vectors corresponding to the ith row vector of S. There are nq matrices of the form $S\&i$ but not all of the total of $(nq)^2$ row vectors in the nq matrices will be different. The upper limit of the number of different such vectors is

$$nq + \frac{nq^2(n-1)}{2}$$

and nq of the vectors are the vectors of S. Thus when considered as a matrix, the vectors of the form $i\&j$ form an

$$nq + \frac{nq^2(n-1)}{2} \times t$$

matrix, nq of the vectors being the vectors of S.

Some of the vectors of the form $i\&j$ may be linearly dependent upon the vectors of S and some may not be. Those vectors linearly independent of the vectors of S indicate that the simplest basis for the vectors of the

$$nq + \frac{nq^2(n-1)}{2} \times t$$

matrix of vectors of the form $i\&j$ may not be the same as the simplest basis for the vectors of S. That the basis for the higher order vectors may be a basis in a higher dimensional space than the basis for the first order vectors is not a serious problem. What is serious is that none of the simplest basis vectors for the vectors of S may be vectors of the simplest basis for the vectors of the augmented matrix, the matrix containing S and the vectors of the form $i\&j$. This possibility suggests that the difference between the simplest basis for S and for S augmented by higher order vectors be investigated.

When row vectors i and j of S are identical then

$$S\&i \equiv S\&j$$

and $\qquad\qquad\qquad S\&iS' \equiv S\&jS'$

When vectors i and j have high cosines, the pairs and triples of occurrences associated with i and j will also be similar. Even when i and j have relatively low inner products, the cosine of $i\&j$ with i and with j will be high relative to the cosine of i and j, for all unit entries in $i\&j$ will be shared by i and j. Thus when the rank of S augmented by the different vectors $i\&j$ is greater than S not so augmented, the length of the images of the $i\&j$ in the subspace defined by the vectors of S will be high in relation to the length of the $i\&j$ in the higher dimensional space.

The vectors generating the quadruples of occurrences may be obtained by taking $S\&i\&j$ and the quadruples of occurrences by taking $S\&i\&jS'$. The rank of each such matrix will be equal to or greater than the rank of S and there will be as many different matrices as there are different combinations $i\&j$, $i\&k$, $i\&m$, etc. It is clear therefore that, for a given S matrix augmented by all of the different vectors from $S\&i$, $S\&i\&j$, $S\&i\&j\&k$, $\ldots$, $S\&i\&j\& \ldots \&nq$ attached, the augmented matrix may have a large number of rows relative to the number of rows in S. That the vectors of S form a subspace in the space defined by the vectors of the augmented matrix is also clear, for the ith row vector of S is also a vector of the form $i\&i$, $i\&i\&i$, etc.

Adopting the convention of calling S a matrix of order one, $S\&i$ a matrix of order two, $S\&i\&j$ a matrix of order three, etc., the ith row vector in $S\&i\&j$ will then be a vector of order three or a third order vector. The ith row vector of the second order matrix $S\&i$ will be a second order vector. The inner product of the jth row vector with itself in a matrix of any order will be equal to or less than the self inner product of those vectors in S contributing to its formations and, in general it will be less.

As with the second order vectors the cosines of the kth row vector of $S\&i\&j$ with the three vectors of S entering into its formation will be higher than with other vectors, for the kth row vector of $S\&i\&j$ has its unit entries in those positions in which the three vectors of S also have unit entries. It follows that projections of all higher order vectors in the subspace defined by S, have lengths which are substantial proportions of their lengths in the higher dimensional space defined by all vectors of all orders.* This can be stated succinctly as follows: The higher order vectors cannot form an orthonormal complete set of vectors unless the data vectors of S form an orthonormal complete set. But when the vectors of S are members of an orthonormal complete set, the higher order vectors are identical with the first order vectors. It follows that when the rank of S exceeds q, any data basis formed from higher order vectors must be an oblique basis. These considerations imply that if S has rank r, then the coordinates of all vectors of all orders on the r vectors of a data basis from S will contain the greater share of the information contained in the coordinates on the $s(s \geq r)$ vectors of the basis for all vectors of all orders. Since the length of the higher order vectors decreases as the order increases, a reduction of the problem can be achieved by using only first and second order vectors in obtaining a simplest basis.† A final

---

* When the projections of the higher order vectors into the subspace defined by S is not a substantial proportion, the higher order vectors are so short as to be negligible.

† T. Koopmans has shown in an unpublished paper that triples of occurrences are sufficient to determine a structure of latent classes. In latent class analysis values analogous to the communalities of factor analysis are used.

reduction of the problem of analysis to one of manageable proportions may be effected by taking a sample, perhaps a random one, of, say, nq of second order vectors and analyzing the $2nq \times t$ augmented matrix.

The analysis of an augmented matrix should proceed in stages. First, the effective rank of S should be determined. This is best accomplished by extracting principal axes. Given an effective rank of r for S, the second order vectors selected may be added to S and r principal axes extracted. The analysis may then proceed as outlined in Chapter 2.

For any particular set of data there is no guarantee that the best data basis for S, the simplest basis, will be the same basis as the simplest basis for the S matrix augmented with higher order vectors. The higher order vectors, being in general shorter than the first order vectors and higher order vectors of a preceding order, will have lower cosines with the Y vector than the vectors of S. Thus the boundary vectors will tend to be higher order vectors. Usually, however, the simple basis for the augmented matrix and for the first order S matrix should be markedly similar when dimensionality is restricted to the dimensionality of the vectors of S. By reason of their manner of formation the higher order vectors must have relatively high cosines with all of the vectors of S used in their formation. The nearer the rank (or the effective rank as determined from the principal axes) of S to q, the number of sub-classes in the classification system, the more likely it is that the simplest basis for S is quite similar to the simplest basis for the vectors of the augmented matrix. In a sense the expression q/r is a measure of the information contained in S. As the expression decreases from unity or above to less than unity and to its lower limit of $q/(qn - n + 1)$, S contains progressively less information about its higher order vectors. Thus q/r can serve as a base for a decision to analyse or not analyse, as the case may be, the higher order vectors. As q/r decreases, so does the index of internal productivity. It seems, therefore, that as the images of the higher order vectors in the subspace defined by S represent the higher order vectors less and less adequately, analysis of the data itself will probably be fruitless because the classification system is unproductive.

CHAPTER SIX

APPLICATIONS

In this chapter we will present the results of exploratory analyses on data from different sources: from a mental test, from verbal behavior in psychotherapy, and from an attitude inventory.

THE HALSTEAD CATEGORY TEST*

The first study to be reported is from an unpublished analysis of data gathered by Simmel and Counts (1957). The 61 subjects of this study originally comprised two samples: 35 patients seen in connection with a study of the effect of temporal lobectomy as a treatment for psychomotor epilepsy and 26 student nurses. Both groups were given the Halstead Category Test, a test designed to measure abstraction or concept formation. The test has been described by Simmel and Counts (1957, p. 7) as follows:

> Briefly, it consists of several groups of visually presented stimulus patterns. For each group a "principle of correct responses" has been defined by the test author and is to be discovered by the subject. The subject's response to each item consists in pressing selectively one of four numbered keys which is in fact equivalent to saying "1", "2", "3", or "4". By means of a chime for correct responses and a buzzer for incorrect responses the subject is continually appraised of the accuracy of his performance and is, in a sense, rewarded and punished.

---

* Communalities were used in the studies reported here. The Halstead Category Test was analyzed by Dr. Sarah Counts.

In comparing the findings on the two groups Simmel and Counts (1957) found that the student nurses made significantly fewer errors, but that the same pattern of item choices prevailed for both groups. This is of import for the current study.   Ordinarily a factor analytic technique should not be undertaken with an N as small as 61 because of the possibility of sampling error sufficient to mask, if not distort, structure.   It was concluded, however, that the prior demonstration of the similarity of item distributions for two quite different groups justified the analysis with 61 subjects.

In this study data from the first sixteen items of Set III of the items in the test were utilized.   However, Sets I and II, and the principles used in getting to correct choices are relevant since they influenced responses to Set III.   Set I has eight items.   Each item consists of one of the first four Roman numerals. S responds correctly if he presses the key corresponding to the same numeral.   For Set II each of the twenty items consists of either one, two, three or four separately articulated figures.   The task for S is to count the number of separate figures and press the corresponding key.   For Sets I and II then, the subject is "encouraged"–first to respond to numerals and then to count the number of figures.

Set III, the set analyzed here, does in fact confront the subjects with a new principle.   Each item in Set III consists of four separate figures.   Throughout the first sixteen items, three of the figures are identical with one differing from the others.   The essential task is to note the difference and that the ordinal position of the differing figures varies from item to item.   If, then, he "numbers" the positions of the four figures from left to right and responds to the position of the odd figure, he can consistently give correct answers.   The subjects quickly note that there are four figures with three alike and one different, and may note that the position of the odd figure varies over items; many, however, fail to appreciate the relevance of the variation of principle leading to correct answers.

It should be noted that the data of this study are different from the type of data discussed so far in that the subject is constrained to make one of four possible responses; the classifications therefore represent actual subject-environment transactions.

Since the third set of items numbered sixteen with four choices each, and since the subjects numbered 61, the S matrix corresponding to the data was 64×61 with a possible rank $(nq - n + 1)$ of 49.

After the Y vector was removed, computations were performed on a digital computer using a centroid program followed by graphical rotation from the first residual matrix, with the highest off-diagonal values being used for communality estimates. Only two basis vectors were retained because the number of subjects was but 61; and the residuals seemed sufficiently low for such a small sample.

The elements of A, the loadings on the simplest basis, and of AQ^{-1}, the loadings normalized to the projections of the Y vector on the simple basis vectors, are shown in Table 13. QR_aQ is shown in Table 14. Since the basis vectors are orthogonal, the classes isolated are mutually exclusive. Note that the solution is unique, since no rotation is possible without obtaining negative numbers. Also the rank differential $r/(nq - n + 1)$ of 0.04 is 96% below the maximum value and the index of internal productivity is 1.00. Hence, we conclude the system possesses considerable productivity.

From Table 13 it is clear that basis vector A_1 is determined by correct answers. Almost all correct answers have high loadings, the only exceptions being the items near the beginning of the sequence of items. Secondly, if alternatives "2" or "4" represent correct choices, then the alternatives lie close to A_1. When "1" and "3" are correct, the choices tend to have substantial loadings on both A_1 and A_2. Turning now to A_2 we find that it is determined by "1" and "3" responses whether correct or incorrect. It would be a mistake to characterize A_2 as a "wrong" class; it will be shown that it is better characterized as a "counting" class. Finally, it should be noted that most of the incorrect "2" and "4" alternatives have loadings on neither factor and have, in fact, low frequencies.

At this point it appears that there are three characteristics which determine loadings on A_1 and A_2 (or $A_1Q_1^{-1}$ and $A_2Q_2^{-1}$).

(a) Right or wrong choice

(b) Choice or response number (q)

(c) Item number (n)

The primary determiner of basis vector A_1 appears to be correct choice of the item alternatives. Therefore, we will call this the "correct class". All alternatives with loadings of 0.40 or higher on $A_1(0.58$ or higher on $A_1Q_1^{-1})$ represent correct responses; conversely all alternatives with loadings less than 0.20 (0.27 on $A_1Q_1^{-1})$ represent

TABLE 13*

LOADINGS OF RESPONSES
ALTERNATIVES ON ORTHONORMAL BASIS VECTORS**
(ENTRIES OF MATRIX A)

	Basis Vector A_1 Alternatives				Basis Vector A_2 Alternatives			
Item	1	2	3	4	1	2	3	4
1	20	00	19	31	04	00	12	57
2	19	02	41	07	18	05	36	14
3	52	00	10	07	11	00	56	05
4	04	02	05	59	23	01	38	10
5	10	47	13	00	09	00	47	16
6	05	00	09	55	18	04	37	13
7	60	00	03	06	22	00	29	22
8	01	67	01	02	28	06	31	05
9	00	00	69	−00	22	07	36	07
10	03	66	01	−06	38	00	29	05
11	−00	01	68	00	25	08	39	00
12	67	00	02	00	26	02	39	04
13	01	00	04	65	29	02	39	01
14	02	−01	67	00	27	10	26	09
15	02	00	02	67	21	00	46	04
16	03	65	01	01	32	08	24	08
	Entries of AQ^{-1}							
1	28	00	27	45	05	00	16	79
2	28	03	58	10	25	07	50	19
3	75	00	15	10	15	00	78	07
4	06	02	08	84	32	01	53	13
5	14	67	18	01	12	01	66	22
6	08	00	13	80	25	06	52	17
7	87	00	05	09	30	00	40	30
8	02	96	01	02	39	08	43	08
9	01	00	99	00	31	09	50	10
10	05	95	00	00	53	00	40	07
11	00	02	98	00	35	11	54	00
12	97	00	03	00	37	03	54	06
13	02	00	06	93	40	03	55	02
14	04	−00	97	00	38	13	37	12
15	03	00	03	96	29	00	64	06
16	04	94	00	00	44	11	33	11

* Decimal points are omitted.

** Underlined alternative is the correct alternative.

TABLE 14*

MATRIX OF PROPORTIONS
FOR EACH CLASS

QR_aQ		
	A_1	A_2
A_1	48	
A_2		52

* Decimal points are omitted.

erroneous responses; and, after the first two trials, all erroneous responses have loadings less than 0.20.

There is one minor exception: 014 (item 1, alternative 4) is greater than 011 (item 1, choice 1), the correct alternative, on A_1. This is the only overlap of loadings between correct and incorrect responses on A_1.

While correctness of response is the necessary condition for an alternative to have a loading on A_1, the size of the loading is related to the place of the item in the sequence of items. Each subject was "rewarded" by a chime for a correct response; "punished" by a buzzer for an incorrect one. Since the later items have the larger loadings on A_1, we can hypothesize that A_1 is determined by those subjects who have learned the principle for correct responses. Thus, although A_1 is determined by correct responses, it seems to be determined by the correct responses of those subjects who have discovered the principle for selecting correct responses. They give *intrinsically* correct responses; A_1 represents the behavior of an "intrinsically correct response" class of subjects.

That it is the incidence of intrinsically correct responses which determines the size of the loading on A_1 can be shown by comparing the magnitude of the loadings on A_1 (or $A_1 Q_1^{-1}$) with the incidence of correct responses. Table 13 shows that particularly for the latter half of the items, alternatives "1" and "3" when correct, have been successfully chosen by ten to fifteen more subjects, on the average, than have items where "2" or "4" are correct. Nevertheless, the loadings in the latter half of the test for "1" and "3" versus "2" and "4" correct alternatives are nearly the same on A_1. Note also that correct responses on the "1" and "3" alternatives are only incidentally correct. This is reflected in the substantial loadings found on A_2 as well as A_1.

By the time Set III of the test, the set under consideration here, has been reached, there are two classes of subjects. One class has grasped the principle of ordinal positions of the different figures of the items and is responding consistently. It is the subject's consistency of performance which actually determines A_1. Subjects in the A_2 class, on the other hand, have not really solved the problem. They give some correct answers but cannot do so consistently and their correct performance does not contribute to the determination of A_1. That is not to say that the performance of the second class is inconsistent or random for this behavior contributes to the determination of A_2. These subjects do, however, increase the incidence of correct responses for those items for which "1" and "3" are correct.

Basis vector A_2 is determined by responses which seems to reflect counting tendencies on the part of the subjects. Therefore A_2 will be called the "counting class" because the responses appear to follow from the counting principle used in attaining correct responses to one of the preceding groups of items. For instance the alternative with the highest loading is 014; 38 subjects gave this response, a simple counting response. (It had been suggested in the instructions that the same principle used before might continue to operate.) On the first item, the majority of subjects continued to count all figures. For the second item, the correct alternative is a "3" response. Hence the subjects were rewarded for using a variation of the counting principle, the type of response which presumably had received reinforcement on the majority of responses made. This reinforcement for counting is reflected in the third and fourth responses: 033, which is high and nearly pure on A_2; and 043, which has the highest frequency among the incorrect alternatives for the fourth item. Throughout the test the highest loadings on A_2 are for "3" responses. The incorrect "3's" are pure on A_2, while the correct ones have substantial loadings on A_1 as well. Thus, it seems safe to conclude that A_2 is generated by a subgroup of the sample using what we call the "counting principle". This conclusion is further substantiated by the "1" responses which are high on A_2, since they represent another counting principle: "one different". Note then that when the "1" and "3" responses are loaded on both A_1 and A_2, the number of correct responses is inflated. Thus, part of the A_1 loadings from "1" correct and "3" correct alternatives are attained through the use of the wrong principle. Conversely, the correct "1" and "3" responses attained by the right principle also inflate the A_2 loadings.

Consideration of QR_aQ shows first that the basis vectors are orthogonal and second that the correct principle class, A_1, and the counting principle class, A_2, have proportions 0.48 and 0.52, respectively.

The protocol of each subject was scored for the number of errors on the A_1 group of items (1, 3, 4, 5, 6, 8, 10, 13, 15, 16), on the A_2 group of items (2, 7, 9, 11, 12, 14) and on all items. There was some question about including the first item in the A_1 group, apart from this all correct responses have high loadings on the class of intrinsically correct responses. The A_2 group of items is the group for which a correct answer may have resulted from an intrinsically correct response or from a counting type of response. The resulting score distributions are shown in Table 15. The distributions for the two groups of items over all subjects are markedly different in shape: for the A_1 items the distribution of scores is bimodal; for the A_2 negatively skewed. For all items the distribution is again bimodal.

Table 15 shows the frequency distribution for the 34 subjects who did not discover the principle of correct response and for the 27 subjects who did. The criterion for selection was the distribution of errors on the ten A_1 items, for there was a clear separation between those subjects making six or more errors on the ten items and those who did not. Table 15 shows rather clearly the two class structure of the items but does not give the detailed information of AQ^{-1}, or of its plot. Note that on the counting items (2, 7, 9, 11, 12, 14) with substantial loadings on A_2 the distribution of the subjects using the counting principle is essentially normal with a modal score of three errors. The group of subjects who demonstrated on the A_1 items that they had grasped the correct principle and were able to give *intrinsically* correct responses have a J distribution on the A_2 items with their modal score at zero errors.*

Other interesting aspects of these distributions emerge when diffi-

---

* There is one exceptional case. This person made four errors on A_1 items and five on A_2 items for a total of nine errors. His protocol shows that in items one through eight he made only one error, to item two; however, beginning with item nine, all responses were incorrect and were all "1" and "3" responses. The prevalence of these responses suggest that he was counting.

TABLE 15

FREQUENCY DISTRIBUTION OF 34 COUNTING SUBJECTS
AND 27 ESSENTIALLY CORRECT SUBJECTS

	No. of Errors	Counting Subjects	Correct Subjects
A_1 Items	10	12	0
	9	12	0
1, 3, 4, 5, 6, 8,	8	5	0
10, 13, 15, 16	7	3	0
	6	2	0
	5	0	0
	4	0	4
	3	0	2
	2	0	7
	1	0	10
	0	0	4
		S 34	S 27
A_2 Items	6	2	0
	5	4	1
2, 7, 9, 11, 12, 14	4	4	0
	3	15	0
	2	7	2
	1	2	9
	0	0	15
		S 34	S 27
All Items		34 Counting Subjects	27 Correct Subjects
	15	2	0
	14	2	0
	13	9	0
	12	12	0
	11	5	0
	10	2	0
	9	1	1
	8	0	0
	7	1	0
	6	0	1
	5	0	1
	4	0	3
	3	0	6
	2	0	3
	1	0	8
	0	0	4
		S 34	S 27

culty levels or percent errors per item are considered. Table 16 shows these results for the intrinsically correct and the counting subjects. The subjects who discover the principle for making correct

TABLE 16

PER CENT ERRORS PER ITEM

	27 Correct Ss	34 Counting Ss
10 A_1 Items	17	89
6 A_2 Items	11	53
16 Items	15	76

responses make approximately the same proportion of errors on both kinds of items. Most of the errors were probably made on the early items of the test before the correct principle had been discovered or before it was consistently applied. For the 34 subjects whose responses reflect counting activity, one might conclude on the basis of ten items that their answers were random; there are four alternatives per item and three-fourths of their responses are incorrect. However, most of their responses to A_1 items are incorrect, but only half of their responses to A_2 items are incorrect. The latter figure corresponds to the expectation based on AQ^{-1}. The A_2 items are those on which "1" or "3" are correct and these subjects tend to respond only with "3" or "1". Under these conditions half of the responses would be expected to be correct.

SUMMARY

The two-class solution is consistent with and supports the findings of Simmel and Counts (1957). These two classes represent "intrinsically correct" and "counting" response dispositions in two groups of subjects. One group contains subjects giving intrinsically correct responses and their consistently correct answers generates class A_1. As the test proceeds more of the subjects are able to give correct answers; thus loadings for the later items rise. The second group of subjects does not solve the problem early in the test. Nevertheless their responses are not random, and in fact are closely related to certain aspects of the stimulus constellations. The interpretation is that they respond with what has been called counting activity.

THE PSYCHOTHERAPY VERBAL STYLE STUDY

The second study to be reported is of quite a different character. Here the verbal behavior of persons in psychotherapy was classified in order to: (1) single out and describe some aspects of clients' verbal therapy behavior; (2) to test the productivity, internal and external, of the classification system which was based on style of participation; and (3) to generate new hypotheses for further study of the psycho-therapeutic process as reflected in client behavior.

Twenty-four completed cases, which had been recorded and tested were selected from a larger research project. Cases were selected to provide equal numbers of interviews from success and failure cases. Therapist rating on a nine point scale was the criterion of success and failure cases. Cases rated six to nine were called success cases; cases rated one to three were called failure cases. Long (more than twenty hours of therapy) and short (less than fifteen hours of therapy) cases were selected in approximate proportion to their appearance within the success and failure groups of the larger population of cases. An additional group of cases (all long) rated five (equivocally successful) was included. Thus the twenty-four cases included five long success cases, four short success cases, four long partially successful cases, three long failure cases, four short failure cases, and four attrition cases (failure cases with four or less interviews.) Cases with more experienced therapists were selected wherever possible within the limits of the other requirements.

The second and next to last therapy hours of each case were selected for analysis, except for the attrition cases where only the second interview was used. Sequences of ten responses each were selected from the first, second, and third thirds of each therapy hour used in the study.

The classification system employed contained three aspects or main classes, each of which was in turn divided into two or more sub-classes. Each response was classified on each aspect, but the sub-classes within each aspect were mutually exclusive. Therefore when tabulated in matrix form, each response of each subject had three unit entries. However when brought into the form of the S matrix (41), each response had just one unit entry; that is, all combinations of sub-classes were found.

The three main aspects of the classification system concerned style of participation rather than specific content. The aspects and their sub-classes are described below.

I. LEVEL OF EXPRESSION

    A. Analysis of Action

        Statements placed here state and analyze, explain or evaluate action, including cognitive action.

    B. Analysis of Feeling

        Statements placed here attempt to analyze, explain, classify, etc., but focus on feelings as inner experience not as classes of behavior.

    C. Responsiveness

        This includes expression of inner experiences — feelings, images, impulses, etc. They are expressed directly rather than being described, analysed, or categorized.

II. INVOLVEMENT

    This aspect involves voice quality alone and is judged on energy, pitch variation, pace, and pattern of emphasis.

    A. Emotional

        There is high energy in the voice, with a quality of discharge or overflow.

    B. Focussed

        The high energy in the voice is turned inward in a pondering, exploring fashion. There are certain irregularities of pace and emphasis, but little fluctuation in pitch.

    C. Externalizing

        High energy in the voice is directed outward with a speech-making quality. The speech pattern is smoother than in B above, with emphatic though often mechanical inflections and a wide range of pitch.

    D. Limited

        Responses placed here are characterized by low energy used in a matter-of-fact fashion. The pace is even and relatively unstressed.

III. Quality of Participation

  A. *Participator*

    This includes responses in which the client is a participator in what he is discussing.

  B. *Observer*

    The client is an observer of the scenes he is describing. For further details on the classification system and its reliability the reader is referred to Wagstaff (1959).

  During the course of the study, it was decided to disregard the sequence of individual responses and use a within-interview sequence comprised of samples of responses from each third of the therapy hour. The S matrix was therefore restructured in such a way as to permit discrimination between thirds of interviews, but not to discriminate between successive responses. However, the fundamental form of matrix S was retained. The data matrix S was of order $nq \times t$ with $n = 30$, $q = 24$, and $t = 44$, n, q, and t indicating respectively, responses, categories, and interviews. That is, S was a 720×44 matrix. Therefore, the maximal possible rank of the data matrix was 44. Since the sampling of interviews was so small compared to the possibilities inherent in the classification system, the analysis was restricted to the study of similarities between interviews. The square symmetric matrix selected for analysis was $(1/n)S'S$ whose entries describe the similarity between the interviews on a scale between zero and unity.

  Matrix $(1/n)S'S$ is shown in Table 17. The odd numbered interviews are early interviews, while the following even numbered interviews are the late interviews of the same case. Thus interview three is the second interview of the second client, while interview four is the next to last interview of the same client. Interviews are grouped as follows: one through ten, long success cases; 11 through 18, short success cases; 19 through 26, long partial success cases; 27 through 32, long failure cases; 33 through 40, short failure cases; 41 through 44, early interviews of attrition cases.

  The matrix $(1/n)S'S$ was reduced by the multiple group method of factor analysis. Two criteria were used for estimating when a sufficient number of basis vectors had been selected: (1) the computation of a sample of 150 residuals, and (2) the sum of squares of the projections of the unit length vector, $S'SY'/\sqrt{n} \sqrt{ZD^2Z'}$ on the basis vectors. When the sum of squares of the projections of this vector reached the value of 0.97, 150 residuals selected randomly were computed. The residuals formed a near-symmetric distribution with a mean of 0.023 and a median of 0.018. Considering that t was 44, no additional basis vectors were selected. Three basis vectors resulted from the analysis.

The three basis vectors had cosines of .24, .18, and .25, and thus were not far from orthogonality. The orthogonalization computing method described in chapter seven was applied with the results shown in Table 18 which shows the inner products of the row vectors of S' with the orthogonal basis vectors approximating the vectors of the simple basis.

With three basis vectors resulting from a matrix whose maximal rank was 44, the rank differential $r/(nq - n + 1)$ is 0.07, a reduction of 93% from the maximal rank possible for $1/nS'S$. The index of productivity was 0.85. The low rank differential and the practically orthogonal structure of R_a as represented by the index of productivity shows the classification system to be internally productive in spite of the small number of interviews.

Descriptions of behavior types I, II, and III (which correspond to the three factors) were obtained by inspecting the columns of the original S matrix representing the behavior of clients whose interviews had loadings of 0.40 or above on one factor and .20 or below on the others.

Type I interviews (Interviews 2, 6, 9, 10) consisted almost entirely of responses classified as Responsiveness or Analysis of Feeling on the first aspect, Emotional or Focussed on the second aspect, and Participating on the third. In terms of the definitions given on p. 77 one could say that clients in Type I interviews are primarily exploring feelings, sometimes attempting to analyze them and occasionally expressing them directly. Voice quality indicates that they maintain an inwardly focussed kind of involvement with occasional emotional overflow. They talk only about matters in which they are clearly participators. There is some suggestion that these interviews become most intense during the middle third, with an increase in direct expression of present feelings and an emotional quality present in the voice.

Type II interviews (Interviews 3, 11, 19, 26, 37, 41) contain primarily responses that are classed as Analysis of Action on the first

TABLE 17

MATRIX $1/n\ S'S$

THE PROPORTIONATE CORRESPONDENCE* BETWEEN INTERVIEWS

	1	2	3	4	5	6	7	8	9	10	11	12	13	14	15	16	17	18	19	20	21	22
1	..																					
2	30	50†																				
3	17	03	..																			
4	23	07	50	..																		
5	20	10	47	33	..																	
6	40	37	23	20	30	36																
7	33	00	50	40	63	23	..															
8	23	00	57	60	33	13	47	..														
9	33	50	10	07	13	43	13	03	51													
10	13	40	00	03	07	37	03	00	33	..												
11	17	07	37	27	37	13	30	43	03	00	44											
12	40	40	13	07	20	30	20	17	37	17	27	..										
13	30	23	23	07	43	50	30	10	37	27	40	43	..									
14	20	23	23	13	33	27	27	17	23	13	57	40	63	..								
15	53	23	20	20	27	40	30	13	40	17	17	33	40	30	..							
16	43	27	23	13	33	57	33	20	30	23	23	40	58	43	47	..						
17	43	03	50	30	47	23	67	50	20	03	27	17	27	20	37	37	..					
18	37	20	20	07	27	43	23	07	33	13	13	37	40	30	43	43	30	..				
19	23	10	40	17	53	27	47	23	17	07	33	33	53	50	27	43	33	27	..			
20	50	27	23	13	37	40	33	20	30	13	33	50	47	43	43	50	30	50	47	..		
21	30	07	47	60	40	23	47	57	07	00	53	20	23	30	20	30	33	17	23	33	..	
22	27	10	63	43	33	23	37	70	07	00	53	20	20	27	20	23	43	17	20	27	60	..
23	37	03	40	53	53	17	73	50	10	00	27	13	13	13	23	20	57	17	23	20	40	30
24	30	07	43	27	53	27	47	40	13	00	47	27	47	43	23	33	30	20	63	40	40	33
25	33	03	33	17	47	33	57	23	10	07	27	23	30	27	30	27	33	23	33	33	30	23
26	13	13	23	10	27	17	23	13	10	00	50	43	47	60	10	30	13	23	40	33	27	27
27	33	03	50	53	63	23	70	60	10	00	33	17	20	23	30	27	50	20	40	33	53	40
28	17	03	63	43	47	27	50	57	07	00	43	13	23	20	20	23	50	27	30	23	47	57
29	37	03	47	53	43	23	57	60	17	00	20	07	13	07	33	27	68	27	30	17	30	33
30	27	00	43	50	33	13	50	67	07	03	17	00	07	03	13	13	57	07	17	03	30	37
31	10	07	37	20	20	53	10	40	27	03	00	53	20	40	53	13	23	30	13	53	30	33
32	33	07	57	57	53	23	70	63	13	03	27	13	13	13	27	27	60	20	20	30	43	40
33	40	13	57	43	50	40	60	40	23	03	30	13	27	20	40	33	60	30	37	23	37	37
34	40	13	47	33	67	33	63	43	23	10	43	40	50	43	37	40	47	30	60	47	40	33
35	43	03	50	47	53	27	73	50	13	00	23	03	10	03	27	23	60	20	30	20	40	37
36	43	03	40	23	40	17	53	33	17	03	37	27	33	23	47	40	57	37	43	53	33	33
37	20	10	30	23	33	17	37	27	17	07	53	40	53	70	23	37	30	23	57	40	37	33
38	20	10	47	30	60	20	60	37	20	03	37	33	47	43	27	40	43	30	60	40	33	30
39	37	03	40	47	53	20	70	50	13	03	27	17	23	30	30	33	53	20	37	23	43	30
40	30	00	37	57	37	13	53	60	10	00	23	10	10	13	20	20	43	10	20	10	43	30
41	20	10	27	20	33	17	30	27	13	03	50	43	47	57	23	37	30	27	50	47	23	27
42	37	10	47	40	57	30	70	40	20	00	33	17	27	20	30	27	63	23	40	30	33	37
43	37	07	43	33	53	27	60	30	17	00	20	10	17	10	27	23	37	30	30	23	33	30
44	30	27	50	43	43	27	43	47	20	07	47	47	43	47	23	40	33	20	47	40	43	50

* Decimal points are omitted.

† Communalities are given only for interviews used in groups.

23	24	25	26	27	28	29	30	31	32	33	34	35	36	37	38	39	40	41	42	43	44	
																						1
																						2
																						3
																						4
																						5
																						6
																						7
																						8
																						9
																						10
																						11
																						12
																						13
																						14
																						15
																						16
																						17
																						18
																						19
																						20
																						21
																						22
69																						23
37	..																					24
53	50	..																				25
10	40	27	61																			26
70	47	43	20	..																		27
43	50	47	30	53	..																	28
67	37	33	03	57	53	70																29
63	30	23	00	53	43	73	68															30
30	47	20	57	47	33	17	20	..														31
70	43	40	13	70	57	70	63	30	..													32
57	43	33	10	57	43	57	50	33	67	..												33
50	63	57	37	60	53	40	30	40	53	47	..											34
77	40	50	00	63	50	70	60	27	77	67	47	..										35
40	47	40	20	43	47	40	23	30	40	37	50	43	..									36
20	43	27	63	33	33	20	10	53	23	20	47	13	40	70								37
50	63	43	43	60	50	43	30	53	57	47	70	47	50	53	..							38
67	43	37	23	70	50	63	60	40	70	53	50	60	37	50	..							39
73	33	40	10	63	40	63	67	23	63	47	40	57	27	23	40	67	67					40
20	40	13	63	27	30	20	10	60	23	20	47	13	37	70	47	27	23	65				41
67	43	40	17	57	43	60	53	33	60	67	57	73	43	27	47	47	43	30	..			42
60	33	43	10	50	37	50	40	33	53	57	40	67	33	23	40	47	47	23	67	..		43
37	47	30	43	47	47	30	27	43	37	37	63	30	43	47	53	37	37	50	40	23	..	44

TABLE 18

ORTHOGONAL APPROXIMATION TO OBLIQUE STRUCTURE
(DATA OF TABLE 18)

Interviews	I	II	III	Interviews	I	II	III
1	.48	.14	.35	24	.15	.50	.35
2	.69	.06	−.04	25	.18	.24	.42
3	.11	.32	.46	26	.12	.78	−.03
4	.10	.18	.62	27	.10	.28	.70
5	.20	.35	.45	28	.10	.38	.50
6	.56	.13	.14	29	.15	.10	.82
7	.10	.30	.67	30	.04	.02	.83
8	.00	.28	.69	31	.01	.72	.19
9	.72	.05	.07	32	.14	.18	.79
10	.56	−.03	−.03	33	.32	.16	.60
11	.03	.63	.19	34	.27	.50	.41
12	.49	.45	.00	35	.15	.05	.79
13	.49	.56	.03	36	.12	.39	.34
14	.28	.78	.00	37	.12	.82	.12
15	.49	.16	.22	38	.16	.53	.42
16	.52	.34	.16	39	.10	.28	.75
17	.16	.24	.63	40	.04	.16	.81
18	.46	.22	.12	41	.10	.80	.12
19	.19	.55	.20	42	.23	.25	.64
20	.44	.45	.07	43	.19	.16	.57
21	.11	.40	.38	44	.29	.55	.31
22	.13	.41	.34	LV	.43	.59	.66
23	.07	.15	.81				

aspect, Limited on the second aspect, and Participating on the third. There is an occasional Analysis of Feeling response. In the final third of the hour the responses are evenly divided on voice quality among Limited, Externalizing, and Focussed. Translated into the definitions on p. 77, this means that clients in Type II interviews are primarily attempting to describe and analyze their own behavior, only very rarely considering feelings and never expressing them directly. Their voice quality throughout the first two-thirds of the interview indicates a limited kind of involvement in what they are saying. During the last third there is an increase of energy in the voice, either focussed inward or with an outward, speech-making quality. In nearly all the responses they are discussing matters in which they are participators.

Type III interviews (Interviews 4, 23, 29, 30, 32, 35, 40, 43) consisted almost entirely of responses classed as Analysis of Action, with only one Analysis of Feeling response in each third of the interview. On the voice quality aspect, Involvement, all but two responses were Externalizing, the other two being Limited. On the third aspect, responses were evenly divided between Participating and Observing. In terms of the definitions on p. 77 one could say that clients in Type III interviews are primarily concentrating on describing and analyzing their own behavior, with rare attempts at analyzing feelings. Feelings are never expressed directly. There is a good deal of energy in the voice, but it is used in an outwardly directed, speechmaking fashion. Occasionally the voice takes on an evener, matter-of-fact quality, but it is never focussed inward, nor is there any expression of emotion. About half the time they are discussing events in which they are participators but the rest of the time they are merely observers of the scene. There are no time trends for thirds of interviews; the client's style of participation does not change as the interview progresses.

In assessing external productivity it was found at the 0.05 level of significance or better that:

1. Both early and late interviews of success cases exhibited more type I behavior than early and later interviews of failure cases.

2. Type II behavior was more characteristic of the late interviews of cases with ratings of five on the nine-point success scale than of late interviews of cases rated as clear-cut successes or failures.

3. Both early and late interviews of failure cases showed more type III behavior than did the success cases.

4. Clients of more experienced therapists exhibited more type I behavior in early interviews and less type III behavior in late interviews than did clients of less experienced therapists.

5. Type I behavior in early interviews correlated .46 (rank order) with favorable changes in self-description on Q-sorts by clients from pretherapy to posttherapy. The same behavior correlated .47 with decrease on Taylor Anxiety Scale scores.

6. Type I behavior in late interviews correlated .39 with post-therapy scores on the Barron Ego-strength scale.
7. Interviews showing high type II behavior correlated .42 with client evaluation of outcome.

TABLE 19*

MATRIX R_0

POLITICAL ATTITUDES

	1	2	3	4	5	6	7	8	9	10	11	12	13	14	15
1	77	00	00	35	31	11	25	25	27	18	50	09	18	49	10
2		12	00	04	07	01	02	07	03	00	08	04	00	10	02
3			11	02	01	08	04	00	07	02	07	02	04	05	02
4				41	00	00	18	10	13	11	25	05	08	25	08
5					39	00	07	20	12	05	29	05	09	27	03
6						20	06	02	12	04	11	05	05	12	03
7							31	00	00	06	19	06	06	21	04
8								32	00	05	22	05	07	20	05
9									37	09	24	04	09	23	05
10										20	00	00	08	09	03
11											65	00	11	51	03
12												15	03	04	08
13													22	00	00
14														64	00
15															14
16															
17															
18															
19															
20															
21															
22															
23															
24															
25															
26															
27															
28															
29															

* Decimal points are omitted.

8. Rank of loadings on types I, II, and III behavior correlated +.60, +.04, and −.60 with rank of frequency of voice quality categories of therapist response which were judged on an a priori basis to be therapeutically optimal.

16	17	18	19	20	21	22	23	24	25	26	27	28	29	
17	32	28	15	44	18	09	59	09	54	23	72	05	00	1
02	06	04	03	07	02	00	10	02	08	04	11	01	00	2
02	04	05	03	04	04	01	06	04	09	02	05	03	03	3
11	13	17	11	21	09	04	29	08	26	15	36	04	01	4
07	24	08	05	27	07	03	35	01	27	12	33	03	02	5
03	05	12	05	07	08	03	11	06	18	02	18	02	00	6
07	12	12	09	15	07	03	24	04	22	09	28	03	00	7
07	17	08	06	23	03	05	26	01	21	11	31	00	01	8
07	13	17	06	17	14	02	25	10	28	09	29	06	02	9
08	10	02	07	08	05	06	08	06	14	06	16	03	01	10
12	28	25	10	42	13	03	57	05	45	20	58	06	01	11
01	04	10	04	05	06	01	10	04	12	03	14	00	01	12
10	08	04	09	08	05	03	13	06	19	03	18	03	01	13
09	30	25	10	43	11	04	56	04	42	22	59	04	01	14
02	04	08	02	04	08	03	06	05	10	04	11	02	01	15
21	00	00	04	11	06	03	13	05	17	04	19	01	01	16
	42	00	07	28	07	05	33	04	29	13	34	06	02	17
		37	10	16	11	02	25	06	25	12	35	02	00	18
			21	00	00	03	16	02	15	06	18	02	01	19
				55	00	05	46	04	48	17	50	04	01	20
					24	02	13	09	18	06	20	03	01	21
						10	00	00	09	01	08	02	00	22
							75	00	59	26	73	02	02	23
								15	13	02	09	05	01	24
									71	00	61	07	03	25
										29	27	02	00	26
											88	00	00	27
												09	00	28
													03	29

* Decimal points are omitted.

THE POLITICAL ATTITUDES STUDY

Our colleagues, Professors David Easton and Robert D. Hess, collected as part of a larger study, data on the ideal political attitudes of high school adolescents. The questionnaire used had items of the form, "A United States senator is personally very much in favor of a bill which the leaders of his party do not want passed. He should (a) vote for the bill, (b) vote against the bill, (c) not vote at all." The items could be construed as requiring the student to choose between two groups of individuals or influences or not to choose at all. From the items, a group of ten judged to be the least ambiguous were selected by Michael Rogin for an exploratory analysis (unpublished). Nine of the ten items had three alternatives; one had but two. The items were coded with respect to the alternatives with Roman numerals to the response alternatives as follows: $\mathbf{I}$ – (1) senator, (2) party, (3) neutral; $\mathbf{II}$ – (4) senator, (5) people, (6) neutral; $\mathbf{III}$ – (7) experts, (8) people, (9) neutral; $\mathbf{IV}$ – (10) friends, (11) senator, (12) neutral; $\mathbf{V}$ – (13) president, (14) senator, (15) neutral; $\mathbf{VI}$ – (16) president, (17) senator, (18) neutral; $\mathbf{VII}$ – (19) pressure, (20) people, (21) neutral; $\mathbf{VIII}$ – (22) advertising campaign convincing voters, (23) senator, (24) neutral; $\mathbf{IX}$ – (25) stay on the job, (26) go home and defend self against attack; $\mathbf{X}$ – (27) senator, (28) neutral, (29) party.

The principle object of the research was to discover the number and nature of different types of ideal images of the manner in which political decisions should be made.

From the 600 respondents, 100 were selected at random. The R_0 matrix of joint proportions for the 29 alternatives is shown in Table 19. Inspection of the matrix revealed that the sums across columns of vectors 4, 9, and 17 gave a column vector with entries proportional to those of the first centroid vector except for the values corresponding to the items for which vectors 4, 9, and 17 were alternatives. These vectors, with corrections underlined, are given in Table 20. The approximately orthogonal basis corresponding to the oblique basis (vectors 4, 9, and 17) and the projections thereon are shown in Table 21.

That the internal productivity of the classification system (items) was high is shown by the rank differential of .13, low compared to its maximum value of unity. The index of internal productivity, not calculated, is obviously above 0.80.

The interpretation of the data analysis which follows is taken from an unpublished study by Michael Rogin. His interpretation is based on Table 21.

<table>
<tr><td colspan="4">TABLE 20*</td></tr>
<tr><td colspan="4">MATRIX $\bar{A}$</td></tr>
<tr><td colspan="4">OF PERPENDICULAR PROJECTIONS</td></tr>
<tr><td colspan="4">ON BASIS VECTORS</td></tr>
<tr><td></td><td>4</td><td>9</td><td>17</td></tr>
<tr><td>1</td><td>35</td><td>37</td><td>42</td></tr>
<tr><td>2</td><td>04</td><td>03</td><td>06</td></tr>
<tr><td>3</td><td>02</td><td>07</td><td>04</td></tr>
<tr><td>4</td><td>23</td><td>13</td><td>13</td></tr>
<tr><td>5</td><td>$\overline{11}$</td><td>12</td><td>24</td></tr>
<tr><td>6</td><td>$\overline{07}$</td><td>12</td><td>05</td></tr>
<tr><td>7</td><td>$\overline{18}$</td><td>07</td><td>12</td></tr>
<tr><td>8</td><td>10</td><td>$\overline{12}$</td><td>17</td></tr>
<tr><td>9</td><td>13</td><td>$\overline{18}$</td><td>13</td></tr>
<tr><td>10</td><td>11</td><td>$\overline{09}$</td><td>10</td></tr>
<tr><td>11</td><td>25</td><td>24</td><td>28</td></tr>
<tr><td>12</td><td>05</td><td>04</td><td>04</td></tr>
<tr><td>13</td><td>08</td><td>09</td><td>08</td></tr>
<tr><td>14</td><td>25</td><td>23</td><td>30</td></tr>
<tr><td>15</td><td>08</td><td>05</td><td>04</td></tr>
<tr><td>16</td><td>11</td><td>07</td><td>07</td></tr>
<tr><td>17</td><td>13</td><td>13</td><td>$\overline{25}$</td></tr>
<tr><td>18</td><td>17</td><td>17</td><td>$\overline{10}$</td></tr>
<tr><td>19</td><td>11</td><td>00</td><td>$\overline{07}$</td></tr>
<tr><td>20</td><td>21</td><td>17</td><td>28</td></tr>
<tr><td>21</td><td>09</td><td>14</td><td>07</td></tr>
<tr><td>22</td><td>04</td><td>02</td><td>05</td></tr>
<tr><td>23</td><td>29</td><td>25</td><td>33</td></tr>
<tr><td>24</td><td>08</td><td>10</td><td>04</td></tr>
<tr><td>25</td><td>26</td><td>28</td><td>29</td></tr>
<tr><td>26</td><td>15</td><td>09</td><td>13</td></tr>
<tr><td>27</td><td>36</td><td>29</td><td>34</td></tr>
<tr><td>28</td><td>04</td><td>06</td><td>06</td></tr>
<tr><td>29</td><td>01</td><td>01</td><td>02</td></tr>
</table>

* Decimal points are omitted.

TABLE 21*

MATRIX, F, OF LOADINGS
ON APPROXIMATE ORTHOGONAL BASIS

Item	Alt.	I	II	III
	1	56	37	44
I	2	06	03	10
	3	−02	16	04
	4	43	15	13
II	5	10	14	44
	6	06	27	01
	7	35	02	17
III	8	10	19	28
	9	14	36	14
	10	14	13	13
IV	11	33	37	44
	12	08	06	05
	13	10	16	15
V	14	34	33	46
	15	15	07	03
	16	19	09	08
VI	17	13	15	45
	18	25	32	06
	19	20	06	08
VII	20	28	20	46
	21	09	30	04
	22	07	00	09
VIII	23	41	35	50
	24	11	21	00
IX	25	32	47	40
	26	26	09	19
	27	55	41	47
X	28	03	11	08
	29	01	01	01
	Y	58	57	58

* Decimal points are omitted.

"The most significant loadings, high and more than double the others, on the first basis vector are 4, 7, 16, and 19. Alternative 15 although having a low loading is pure on this basis vector. Alternatives 4, 7, and 16 suggest that the first type is characterized by choice against the people wherever that choice is permitted by the questionnaire. Alternative 18 suggests a refusal to choose between the senator and the president. It seems that the type represents a choice of authority figures over the people."

"The third basis vector (high and pure loadings on 5 and 17) is characterized by the choice of the senator or the people over the president. This suggests that, associated with the ideal of popular sovereignty, which is clearly the basic characteristic of this type, is the ideal of the rational man, free from pressure, who makes up his mind on the basis of the issues. It should be noted that neutral alternatives tend not to have loadings on the third basis vector. The items having their highest loading on this basis vector dominantly indicate what might be called the combined ideal of popular sovereignty and the rational man."

"The pure loadings on the second basis vector (6, 9, 21, and 24) consist of refusal to choose between the people and authority. These alternatives represent three or four such possible choices. This result supports the interpretation that the conflict between people and authority is the main value tested by these questions. Response sets or apathy seem not to suffice to account for the second type. Rather what is suggested is that 'mass politics' results in dislike of or withdrawal from 'mass' machine politics and 'rational popular sovereignty'."

"The data suggest that there is a continuum with popular sovereignty at one extreme (as an ideal) and authority at the other. The senator represents for respondents at both extremes, the independent rational man acting on the basis of the issues on the one hand and authority on the other. The senator is perceived by one group as the bulwark of authority and by the other as the bulwark of democracy. Thus the interesting fact that the senator alternative is chosen more often than one would expect whenever the choice is ambiguous between authority and democracy, as often it must be. Although these respondents were adolescent students, the data suggest why the senator has so much prestige and influence in our society. His image is congenial to groups whose images of each other are negative."

TABLE 22*

Matrix FQ^{-1}

Item	Alt.	I	II	III
	1	96	65	76
I	2	10	07	17
	3	−04	28	07
	4	74	26	22
II	5	17	25	76
	6	10	47	02
	7	60	03	29
III	8	17	33	48
	9	24	63	24
	10	24	23	22
IV	11	57	65	76
	12	14	10	09
	13	17	28	26
V	14	59	58	79
	15	26	12	05
	16	33	16	14
VI	17	22	26	76
	18	43	56	10
	19	35	10	14
VII	20	48	35	79
	21	16	53	07
	22	12	00	09
VIII	23	71	61	86
	24	19	36	00
IX	25	55	82	69
	26	45	16	33
	27	95	72	81
X	28	05	19	14
	29	02	02	02
	Y	1.00	1.00	1.00

* Decimal points are omitted.

TABLE 23

Matrix, QQ, of Class Proportions

34		
	32	
		34

COMMENTS ON APPLICATIONS

Of the applications of exploratory analysis offered, only the analysis of psychotherapeutic interviews exemplifies the naturalistic observation of free, uncontrolled behavior. Subjects taking the Halstead test were limited to answering one of four possible alternatives. Since answers were rewarded by a chime and punished by a buzzer for correct and incorrect responses, respectively, a learning situation with limited and standardized response alternatives was being studied. A closer analysis of the coordinates of the data vectors would possibly have revealed some effects of alternating reinforcement on the different alternatives. The usual factor analytic procedure, based on a 16×16 matrix, because of dichotomous scoring, would have revealed the growing ability of the subjects to grasp the principle underlying correct responses. In the present analysis the first factor was detected as a simplex and it appears that the method of analysis here used may identify sub-matrices of simplexes in data matrices. The usual factor analysis would not have revealed systematic pattern in the wrong answers for the simple reason that the wrong answers would have been condensed by implication at least into a "not-correct" class. The difference in type of result to be expected is due entirely to the fact that in conventional factor analysis of items, the focus is upon the correct or "positive" responses; thus, except in the dichotomous case, eliminating all regularities in response except among a specially designated sub-class of behavior. Even in the dichotomous case, the usual factor analytic procedure does not use whatever information is contained in the first principal axis of the total data matrix which shows explicitly the classes of responses collectively designated as incorrect.

The use of factor analysis in the study of attitude items requires a judgment that a certain sub-class of response is "ideal," "optimal," "good," etc., such norms usually being collectively designated as positive. No study has yet been conducted in the knowledge of the writers in which the sub-collection of positive responses was designated as positive by resort to a table of random numbers although it would be possible to do so. While normative decisions as to what sub-class of responses to analyze cannot be criticized as such, these decisions to restrict analysis to $1/q$ of q categories of response might be viewed as one of the possible outcomes of analysis rather than as preliminary to analysis. After all the classification system itself is in part a product of normative decisions; it seems desirable to minimize such decisions to the extent possible because such decisions are risky. The greater the number of classes in the classification system the more risk is attached to selecting for analysis just one of the classes.

In the study of psychotherapeutic interviews the classification system contained twenty-four main sub-classes. The usual factor analytic procedure would have required some decision as to which one of the twenty-four categories represented, for example, the optimal class of response, the remaining twenty-three categories being relegated to the non-optimal class for purposes of analysis. The resulting data matrix would then have had but twenty-four rows, had a row analysis of the data matrix been done. But the entire classification system itself was based on the investigator's opinions as to what was optimal or non-optimal and the sub-categories represented judgments of various levels of optimality. One main purpose of the analysis was to ascertain from the relations among responses, categories, and criteria those sub-classes of behavior which were optimal and non-optimal.

APPENDIX A: TESTS OF SIGNIFICANCE FOR THE NUMBER OF BASIS VECTORS

In some situations it is to be expected that for a given set of responses, n, and for a given number of subjects, t, no sequence effects will be observed or are expected. This situation holds for some types of conversations, achievement and aptitude tests, and personality and attitude inventories. When such is the case the summary matrix $\sum_1^n S_i$ may be analyzed. There are n matrices S_i, each of the S_i being $q \times t$. The row vectors of $\sum_1^n S_i$ are the centroids of the q sub-classes of the classification system. The total χ^2 with $(q-1)(r-1)$ degrees of freedom is

$$\chi_t^2 = nt(s-1) \tag{1}$$

where n is the number of responses, t the number of subjects, and s is the sum of the diagonal elements of

$$U = 1/n \left(\sum_1^n S_i \sum_1^n S_i' \right) D^{-1} - W \tag{2}$$

with D being the diagonal matrix whose elements are the column (or row) sums of $1/n\left(\sum_1^n S_i \sum_1^n S_i' \right)$ and with W being the $q \times q$ matrix with elements $1/q$, q being the number of categories in the classifications system. The value of χ_2^2, associated with the second latent root, is given by

$$\chi_2^2/nt = \frac{x \left[D^{-1/2} \, (1/n) \sum_1^n S_i \sum_1^n S_i' D^{-1/2} \right] x'}{xDx'} \tag{3}$$

where x is the second latent vector expressed as a row matrix. Denoting the correlation ratio by η_2^2, (3) becomes

$$\chi_2^2 = nt \, \eta_2^2 \tag{4}$$

Besides being a correlation ratio η_2^2 is the second latent root of $D^{-1/2} \, (1/n) \sum_1^n S_i \sum_1^n S_i' \, D^{-1/2}$. Upon taking each additional latent root two degrees of freedom are lost. The partition of χ^2 is shown below

PARTITION OF χ^2

Roots	d.f.	χ^2
η_2^2	$(q-1) + (t-1)$	$nt\eta_2^2$
η_3^2	$(q-1) + (t-1) - 2$	$nt\eta_3^2$
Remaining Roots	(by subtraction)	(by subtraction)
Total	$(q-1)(t-1)$	$nt(s-1)$

When the remaining roots are significant there remain additional significant dimensions and other latent vectors may be extracted. However, the per cent of the total accounted for may, at times, be so high as to make extraction of additional vectors unprofitable.

When η_2^2 is the only significant correlation ratio, one dimension accounts for the data under the hypothesis that there is an underlying scale. Then taking

$$(1/n) - G \sum_1^n S_i \tag{5}$$

where G is a diagonal matrix whose elements are the elements of the second latent vector and transforming the entries of (5) to zero mean and unit variance (i.e., to standard scores) gives a set of weights for each category of the classification system which best discriminates among subjects in the sense of least squares. For r latent vectors, there will be $(r-1)$ sets of scores, the first latent vector, the trivial vector, not being used. The scores for each subject are obtained by summing down the columns of (5).

The scores being optimal in the sense of least squares, no other set of weights will be better than the weights of (5). However, other sets of weights may be as good or almost so. In particular weights for categories derived from orthogonal bases approximating simplest bases can be expected to provide effective weights and scores for subjects.

The number of significant latent roots plus one of $\sum_{1}^{n} S_i$ can serve as an estimate of the rank of S albeit a very conservative one. However, one can be sure that if $\sum_{1}^{n} S_i$ has r significant latent roots, then S has rank of at least $r + 1$.

A detailed consideration of tests of significance for latent roots is given by Bock (1956).

APPENDIX B: PROOF THAT THE SEQUENCE OF MATRICES $R_a, R_1, \ldots, R_n$ CONVERGES TO AN IDENTITY MATRIX

L. HARMON HOOK
UNIVERSITY OF CHICAGO

Suppose we are given a symmetric positive definite matrix whose elements are the inner products of the appropriate unit basis vectors, i.e.,

$$R_a = \begin{bmatrix} (\alpha_1, \alpha_1) & (\alpha_1, \alpha_2) & \ldots & (\alpha_1, \alpha_n) \\ (\alpha_2, \alpha_1) & \cdot & & \cdot \\ & \cdot & \cdot & \cdot \\ & \cdot & \cdot & \cdot \\ & \cdot & \cdot & \cdot \\ (\alpha_n, \alpha_1) & (\alpha_n, \alpha_2) & \ldots & (\alpha_n, \alpha_n) \end{bmatrix}$$

By the Gram-Schmidt orthogonalization process or equivalently by the diagonal factoring method, we may obtain an orthonormal basis $\epsilon_1, \epsilon_2, \ldots, \epsilon_n$ defined as follows:

$$\epsilon_1 = \alpha_1/\|\alpha_1\|$$

$$\epsilon_2 = [\alpha_2 - (\alpha_2, \epsilon_1)\epsilon_1]/\|\alpha_2 - (\alpha_2, \epsilon_1)\epsilon_1\|$$

$$\ldots \ldots \ldots \ldots \ldots \ldots \ldots \ldots \ldots \ldots \ldots$$

$$\epsilon_j = [\alpha_j - \sum_{i=1}^{j-1} (\alpha_j, \epsilon_i)\,\epsilon_i]/\|\alpha_j - \sum_{i=1}^{j-1} (\alpha_j, \epsilon_i)\epsilon_i\|.$$

We also have,

$$\alpha_1 = (\alpha_1, \epsilon_1)\epsilon_1 + 0 \cdot \epsilon_2 + \ldots + 0 \cdot \epsilon_n$$

$$\alpha_2 = (\alpha_2, \epsilon_1)\epsilon_1 + (\alpha_2, \epsilon_2)\epsilon_2 + 0 \cdot \epsilon_3 + \ldots + 0 \cdot \epsilon_n$$

.

.

.

$$\alpha_n = (\alpha_n, \epsilon_1)\epsilon_1 + \ldots + (\alpha_n, \epsilon_n)\epsilon_n.$$

It is now possible to find unit length vectors $\delta_1, \delta_2, \ldots, \delta_n$ such that

$$(\delta_i, \alpha_j) = \begin{cases} C_j > 0, i = j \\ 0 \quad\quad, i \neq j \end{cases}$$

for $\quad\quad i, j = 1, 2, \ldots, n.$ Clearly, we have

$$\delta_1 = (\delta_1, \epsilon_1)\epsilon_1 + (\delta_1, \epsilon_2)\epsilon_2 + \ldots + (\delta_1, \epsilon_n)\epsilon_n$$

$$\delta_2 = (\delta_2, \epsilon_1)\epsilon_1 + (\delta_2, \epsilon_2)\epsilon_2 + \ldots + (\delta_2, \epsilon_n)\epsilon_n$$

.

.

.

$$\delta_n = (\delta_n, \epsilon_1)\epsilon_1 + (\delta_n, \epsilon_2)\epsilon_2 + \ldots + (\delta_n, \epsilon_n)\epsilon_n.$$

Let $\quad\quad \gamma_i' = \alpha_i + \delta_i, i = 1, 2, \ldots, n;$

and let $\gamma_i = \gamma_i'/\|\gamma_i'\|$, i.e., γ_i is a unit vector in the direction of γ_i' or is γ_i' normalized.

We are interested in the inner product

$$(\gamma_i, \gamma_j) = (\gamma_i', \gamma_j')/\|\gamma_i'\| \cdot \|\gamma_j'\|$$

$$= (\alpha_i + \delta_i, \alpha_j + \delta_j)/\|\alpha_i + \delta_i\| \cdot \|\alpha_j + \delta_j\| \cdot$$

For $i = j$, this inner product is seen to always be unity. In what follows, assume that $i \neq j$. Then

$$(\gamma_i, \gamma_j) = \frac{1}{\|\alpha_i + \delta_i\| \cdot \|\alpha_j + \delta_j\|} \left[(\alpha_i, \alpha_j) + (\alpha_i, \delta_j) + (\alpha_j, \delta_i) + (\delta_i, \delta_j) \right];$$

but $(\alpha_i, \delta_j) = 0$ for $i \neq j$ by construction, so if

$$K = \frac{1}{\|\alpha_i + \delta_i\| \cdot \|\alpha_j + \delta_j\|},$$

we have

$$(\gamma_i, \gamma_j) = K[(\alpha_i, \alpha_j) + (\delta_i, \delta_j)].$$

It should be observed that the vectors $\gamma_1, \gamma_2, \ldots, \gamma_n$ constitute a basis for the same space for which $\alpha_1, \alpha_2, \ldots, \alpha_n$ are a basis. Thus we can obtain a matrix R_1 similar to R_a in the sense that it is a symmetric positive definite matrix whose elements are the inner products of the basis vectors $\gamma_1, \gamma_2, \ldots, \gamma_n$, viz.:

$$R_1 = \begin{bmatrix} (\gamma_1, \gamma_1) & (\gamma_1, \gamma_2) & \cdots & (\gamma_1, \gamma_n) \\ (\gamma_2, \gamma_1) & (\gamma_2, \gamma_2) & \cdots & (\gamma_2, \gamma_n) \\ & \cdot & & \\ & \cdot & & \\ & \cdot & & \\ (\gamma_n, \gamma_1) & (\gamma_n, \gamma_2) & \cdots & (\gamma_n, \gamma_n) \end{bmatrix}.$$

Since

$$(\gamma_i, \gamma_j) = K[(\alpha_i, \alpha_j) + (\delta_i, \delta_j)]$$

there is some relationship between these two matrices. In particular if $(\delta_i, \delta_j) < 0$, then the basis $\gamma_1, \gamma_2, \ldots, \gamma_n$ is in general a basis closer to being an orthogonal basis than the basis $\alpha_1, \alpha_2, \ldots, \alpha_n$. Again, if the above steps are repeated using R_1 in place of R_a, we should obtain new vectors $^{(2)}\gamma_1, {}^{(2)}\gamma_2, \ldots, {}^{(2)}\gamma_n$ constituting a basis for the space of which $\alpha_1, \alpha_2, \ldots, \alpha_n$ is a basis and having the property that it is a more nearly orthogonal basis than that of $\gamma_1, \gamma_2, \ldots, \gamma_n$.

The remaining arguments will indicate that repetition of the above steps will indeed lead to a unique orthonormal basis for the same space as that for which $\alpha_1, \alpha_2, \ldots, \alpha_n$ is a basis. Further properties of this uniquely determined basis will be examined later.

Returning to a more exact discussion, we have the following hypotheses:

$$* \begin{cases} (\alpha_i, \alpha_j) \geq 0 \text{ for all } i \text{ and } j \\ (\delta_i, \alpha_j) = \begin{cases} C_j > 0, i = j \\ 0 \quad , i \neq j, \end{cases} \end{cases}$$

and we want to see what restrictions these hypotheses impose on (δ_i, δ_j). For a particular i and j let

$$M = \{\alpha_k; k = 1, \ldots, n; k \neq i; k \neq j\}$$

be the subspace whose basis consists of all the $\alpha_1, \alpha_2, \ldots, \alpha_n$ except α_i and α_j for the particular i and j selected above. By construction:

$$\delta_i \perp M \text{ and } \delta_j \perp M.$$

In conjunction with hypothesis ✽, this implies that

$$\delta_i \perp \{M, \alpha_j\} \text{ and } \delta_j \perp \{M, \alpha_i\}.$$

Thus, when $\delta_i \perp \delta_j$, we must have

$$\delta_i \in \{M, \alpha_i\}$$

as $\delta_j \perp \{M, \alpha_i\}$ and as $\{\delta_j, \alpha_i, M\}$ generate the entire space. As $\delta_i \perp M$, δ_i is a scalar multiple of α_i. However, since both are unit vectors and chosen in the same direction

$$\delta_i = \alpha_i.$$

By symmetry, a similar argument is valid for δ_j, and we have

$$\delta_j = \alpha_j.$$

Thus, $(\alpha_i, \alpha_j) = (\delta_i, \delta_j) = 0$ when it is supposed that $(\delta_i, \delta_j) = 0$.

The converse of the above argument is trivial due to the construction of the δ_i. Thus, we conclude that $\alpha_i \perp \alpha_j$ if and only if $\delta_i \perp \delta_j$. This implies that if we originally have orthogonal basis vectors α_i and α_j, we shall already obtain orthogonal basis vectors γ_i and γ_j because

$$(\gamma_i, \gamma_j) = K[(\alpha_i, \alpha_j) + (\delta_i, \delta_j)]$$
$$= K \cdot 0$$
$$= 0.$$

Having dispensed with this case, we may change our hypotheses ✽ to read

$$✽' \quad \begin{cases} (\alpha_i, \alpha_j) > 0 \text{ for all } i \text{ and } j \\ (\delta_i, \alpha_j) = \begin{cases} C_j > 0, \, i = j \\ 0 \quad\;\;, \, i \neq j. \end{cases} \end{cases}$$

Using the same notation as above, let us treat the case

Case 1: $\alpha_i \perp M$ and $\alpha_j \perp M$.

In this case α_i, α_j, δ_i and δ_j all lie in the same 2-space, i.e., they are all in one plane.

Project α_i into $\{\alpha_j\}^\perp$, i.e., the subspace of the 2-space orthogonal to the subspace generated by α_j, and call this projection δ_i'; similarly, project α_j into $\{\alpha_i\}^\perp$ and call this projection δ_j'.

Construct δ_i such that

$$\delta_i = \delta_i'/\|\delta_i'\|,$$

i.e., δ_i is colinear with δ_i' and is of unit length. Similarly, construct δ_j colinear with δ_j' and of unit length.

Now let

$$\gamma_i' = \alpha_i + \delta_i$$

and

$$\gamma_j' = \alpha_j + \delta_j.$$

Also let

$$\gamma_i = \gamma_i'/\|\gamma_i'\|$$

and

$$\gamma_j = \gamma_j'/\|\gamma_j'\|.$$

Now consider

$$
\begin{aligned}
(\gamma_i, \gamma_j) &= (\alpha_i + \delta_i,\ \alpha_j + \delta_j) \\
&= (\alpha_i, \alpha_j) + (\delta_i, \delta_j) \\
&= \|\alpha_i\| \cdot \|\alpha_j\| \cos \theta \\
&\quad + \|\delta_i\| \cdot \|\delta_j\| \cos \phi, \\
&= \cos \theta + \cos \phi
\end{aligned}
$$

because α_i, α_j, δ_i and δ_j are all of unit length, where the angle θ is the acute angle between α_i and α_j and ϕ is the angle between δ_i and δ_j.

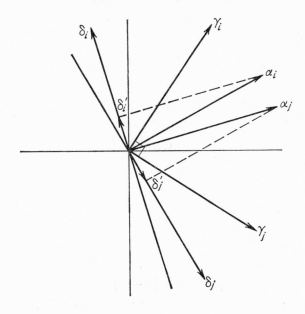

Referring to the diagram, we have

$$\phi = \pi - \theta$$

and

$$\cos \phi = -\cos \theta.$$

Thus, $$(\gamma_i, \gamma_j) = 0 = (\alpha_i, \alpha_j) + (\delta_i, \delta_j)$$

and $$(\delta_i, \delta_j) = -(\alpha_i, \alpha_j)$$

or $$(\delta_i, \delta_j) < 0 \text{ as } (\alpha_i, \alpha_j) > 0 \text{ by hypothesis.}$$

Let us now consider the following less restrictive case

Case 2: $\alpha_i \perp M$ and α_j not $\perp M$.

Since $$(\alpha_i, \delta_i) = C_i > 0$$

and $$(\alpha_i, \delta_j) = 0,$$

we can write δ_i as a linear combination of α_i and δ_j, i.e.,

$$\delta_i = a_i\alpha_i + a_j\delta_j;$$

and since $$(\alpha_i, \delta_i) = c_i = a_i(\alpha_i, \alpha_i) + a_j(\alpha_i, \delta_j)$$

$$= a_i,$$

we have $a_i > 0$. Also,

$$(\delta_i, \delta_j) = a_i(\alpha_i, \delta_j) + a_j(\delta_j, \delta_j)$$

$$= a_j.$$

Suppose $a_j > 0$. Then $(\alpha_j, \delta_i) = 0$ implies that

$$(\alpha_j, a_i \cdot \alpha_i + a_j \cdot \delta_j) = a_i(\alpha_i, \alpha_j) + a_j(\alpha_j, \delta_j)$$

$$= 0.$$

Thus, since $(\alpha_j, \delta_j) > 0$, $(\alpha_i, \alpha_j) > 0$, and $a_i > 0$, we must have $a_j < 0$ which is a contradiction. We must then conclude that

$$a_j = (\delta_i, \delta_j) < 0$$

as before.

The most general case is

Case 3: α_i not $\perp M$ and α_j not $\perp M$.

Let P be the projection into $\{\delta_i, \delta_j\}$ along M, i.e., the orthogonal projection onto the subspace generated by δ_i and δ_j. Let I be the identity operator. Thus, for $\gamma \epsilon M$, $P\gamma = 0$ and for any vector β,

$$\beta = P\beta + (I - P)\beta,$$

where $P\beta$ is in the 2-space $\{\delta_i, \delta_j\}$ and $(I - P)\beta$ is in M.

In particular, $(\alpha_i, \delta_j) = 0$ implies that

$$(\alpha_i, \delta_j) = (P\alpha_i, \delta_j) + [(I - P)\alpha_i, \delta_j]$$

$$= (P\alpha_i, \delta_j)$$

since $\delta_j \perp M$ and $(I - P)\alpha_i$ is in M.   Thus, $(\alpha_i, \delta_j) = 0$ implies that $(P\alpha_i, \delta_j) = 0$.

We may now apply Case 2 to $P\alpha_i$, α_j, δ_i and δ_j.   Similar arguments show that

$$\delta_i = b_i P\alpha_i + b_j \delta_j$$

and

$$\begin{aligned}(\delta_i, P\alpha_i) &= b_i(P\alpha_i, P\alpha_i) + b_j(\delta_j, P\alpha_i) \\ &= b_i(P\alpha_i, P\alpha_i).\end{aligned}$$

Also,

$$\begin{aligned}0 < C_i = (\delta_i, \alpha_i) &= (\delta_i, P\alpha_i + (I - P)\alpha_i) \\ &= (\delta_i, P\alpha_i) + (\delta_i, (I - P)\alpha_i) \\ &= (\delta_i, P\alpha_i)\end{aligned}$$

since $(I - P)\alpha_i$ is in M and $\delta_i \perp M$.   Hence,

$$0 < C_i = b_i(P\alpha_i, P\alpha_i);$$

and since $(P\alpha_i, P\alpha_i) > 0$, we must have $b_i > 0$.   Thus, Case 2 is applicable and once again we conclude that

$$(\delta_i, \delta_j) < 0.$$

We have just shown that in all possible cases $(\delta_i, \delta_j) < 0$.   Hence, since

$$(\gamma_i, \gamma_j) = K[(\alpha_i, \alpha_j) + (\delta_i, \delta_j)],$$

we must have

$$(\gamma_i, \gamma_j) < (\alpha_i, \alpha_j)$$

as $K > 0$.   Also

$$0 \leq |(\gamma_i, \gamma_j)| < (\alpha_i, \alpha_j).$$

APPENDIX C: THE SPECIAL CASE
OF THE DICHOTOMY

The case of the dichotomy is one of special interest because it has been treated extensively by Lazarsfeld (1957), Green (1953), Gibson (1951), and others in connection with latent class analysis (Lazarsfeld, 1957). There are two formally similar but different cases of the dichotomous classification. In one case the classification system has just two sub-categories. In the other the classification system may have more than two categories but the investigator reduces the system to a dichotomy by deciding to classify one of the sub-categories as the "correct" or "positive" or "desirable" or the "most interesting" category. Such concentration on a single category is equivalent to selecting an $n \times t$ sub-matrix corresponding to a single response. In other words a sub-set of the data is selected for analysis.

In latent class analysis it is postulated that a population of subjects can be divided into r classes, the key characteristic of the r classes being that for the subjects in each class the responses to the n dichotomous items are statistically independent. Thus the most important assumption is that the probability of a set of responses of a subject belonging to one of the r classes is the product of the probabilities of the responses to each item of the set. The equations of latent class analysis may be written as follows:

$$1 = p_\mathrm{I} + p_\mathrm{II} + p_\mathrm{III} + \ldots + p_\lambda$$

$$p_i = p_\mathrm{I} p_{\mathrm{I}i} + p_\mathrm{II} p_{\mathrm{II}i} + \ldots + p_\lambda p_{\lambda i}$$

$$p_{ij} = p_\mathrm{I} p_{\mathrm{I}i} p_{\mathrm{I}j} + p_\mathrm{II} p_{\mathrm{II}i} p_{\mathrm{II}j} + \ldots + p_\lambda p_{\lambda i} p_{\lambda j}$$

$$p_{ijk} = p_\mathrm{I} p_{\mathrm{I}i} p_{\mathrm{I}j} p_{\mathrm{I}k} + p_\mathrm{II} p_{\mathrm{II}i} p_{\mathrm{II}j} p_{\mathrm{II}k} + \ldots + p_\lambda p_{\lambda i} p_{\lambda j} p_{\lambda k}$$

etc., where the expressions on the left are empirical proportions and those on the right are theoretical. These are I, II, . . ., λ latent classes. When expressed in matrix notation all cells with recurring subscripts represent theoretical values; those with non-recurring subscripts, empirical.

The matrices of empirical joint proportions of whatever order can be derived from either the reduced $n \times t$ sub-matrix or from the full dichotomized S matrix. When the full $2n \times t$ dichotomized S matrix is used the matrix of joint proportions corresponding to pairs contains the empirical proportions P_{ii} in the diagonals and zero in the off-diagonal cells of the principal sub-matrices corresponding to the n_i. In latent class analysis other values, analogous to the communalities of factor analysis must be used. These values then limit the entries appearing in the diagonals of the matrices of higher order joint proportions and in certain of the off-diagonal cells. In a matrix of proportions corresponding to the triples, the general element is P_{ijk} but some elements with recurring subscripts P_{iik}, etc., will appear. Such elements must be estimated unless the data are treated asymmetrically. At the present stage of development of the subject this involves treating only part of the data. Thus when data are dichotomized (rather than being "naturally dichotomous"), there is a selection among the data vectors which disregards information by selecting n from among nq data vectors; then a further selection must be made in order to avoid estimating unknown values. On the other hand, if all of the data are to be used, then far more than the nq values to be substituted in the diagonals of R_0 must be estimated. Finally, as in factor analysis using communalities, the statistical rank of R_0 with communalities in the diagonals must be estimated.

In view of the fact that the data of S matrices can be changed into dichotomous classes, latent class analysis can be considered to be an alternative to the analysis of empirical S matrices. It seems, therefore, appropriate to compare an analysis of an R_0 matrix for which the true latent structure is known with a latent class analysis of the same data.

Table 1 shows an R_0 matrix for data with three latent classes. The non-empirical values, necessary for latent class analysis, are underlined. The true latent structure is shown in Tables 2 and 3. The structure arrived at by analyzing R_0 *only* with empirical values in the diagonals and in the underlined off-diagonal entries is shown in

TABLE 1

Fictitious Data Matrix R_0^* ($q = 2$, $n = 10$)

	1	2	3	4	5	6	7	8	9	10	11	12	13	14	15	16	17	18	19	20	Y	
1	272	228	175	325	306	194	233	267	217	283	183	317	374	126	260	240	124	376	307	193	500	1
2	228	272	115	385	234	266	197	303	133	367	147	353	326	174	260	240	196	304	223	277	500	2
3	175	115	126	164	198	092	131	159	163	127	120	170	233	057	140	150	055	235	208	082	290	3
4	325	385	164	546	342	368	299	411	187	523	210	500	467	243	380	330	265	445	322	388	710	4
5	306	234	198	342	347	193	270	270	246	294	204	336	414	126	288	252	114	426	348	192	540	5
6	194	266	092	368	193	267	160	300	104	356	126	334	286	174	232	228	206	254	182	278	360	6
7	233	197	131	299	270	160	246	184	155	275	150	280	419	011	256	174	089	341	254	176	430	7
8	267	303	159	411	270	300	184	386	195	375	180	390	381	289	264	306	231	339	276	294	570	8
9	217	133	163	187	246	104	155	195	211	139	150	200	287	063	164	186	061	289	262	088	350	9
10	283	367	127	523	294	350	275	375	139	511	180	470	413	237	356	294	259	391	268	382	650	10
11	183	147	120	210	204	126	150	180	150	180	122	208	249	081	168	162	081	249	207	123	330	11
12	317	353	170	500	336	334	280	390	200	470	208	462	512	219	352	318	239	431	272	248	670	12
13	374	326	233	467	414	286	419	381	287	413	249	451	512	188	364	336	188	512	413	347	700	13
14	126	174	057	243	126	174	011	289	063	237	081	219	188	112	156	144	132	168	117	183	300	14
15	260	260	140	380	288	232	256	264	164	356	168	352	364	156	291	229	152	368	272	248	520	15
16	240	240	150	330	252	228	174	306	186	294	162	318	336	144	229	251	168	312	258	222	480	16
17	124	196	055	265	114	206	089	231	061	259	081	239	188	132	152	168	166	154	109	211	320	17
18	376	304	235	445	426	254	341	339	289	391	249	431	512	168	368	312	154	526	421	259	680	18
19	307	223	208	322	348	182	254	276	262	268	207	272	413	117	272	258	109	421	354	176	530	19
20	193	277	082	388	192	278	176	294	088	382	123	248	347	183	248	222	211	259	176	294	470	20
Y	500	500	290	710	540	460	430	570	350	650	330	670	700	300	520	480	320	680	530	470	1.00	Y

* Decimal points are omitted.

Tables 4 and 5.   The solution of Table 5 was arrived at by taking the principal axes of R_0, identifying the vectors of the oblique simplest data basis and orthogonalizing on the oblique simplest basis.   Comparison of the structures shows clearly their essential similarity although magnitudes differ.   The degree of similarity probably could be increased by further rotation.   The number of basis vectors selected by using the principal axes is three and the correspondingly numbered row vectors have the same patterns of high and low inner products.   For purposes of hypothesis formation and inference it would seem that the two approaches give similar structures for dichotomized or dichotomous data.

TABLE 2

LATENT STRUCTURE* L

	I	II	III
0	548	547	632
1	164	383	316
3	055	328	126
5	109	438	379
7	055	219	442
9	055	438	126
11	109	273	190
13	273	492	442
15	219	219	442
17	383	055	126
19	109	492	316

* Decimal points omitted.

TABLE 3

LATENT STRUCTURE* N

I	I	II	III
I	30		
II		30	
III			40

* Decimal points omitted.

TABLE 4*

STRUCTURE DERIVED FROM R_0

1	164	433	285
3	039	340	129
5	113	461	379
7	014	177	545
9	038	441	136
11	100	296	167
13	244	462	558
15	229	135	530
17	400	044	096
19	111	531	305

* Decimal points omitted.

TABLE 5*

QRQ		
37		
	30	
		35

* Decimal points omitted.

APPENDIX D: ANALYSIS OF

WEIGHTED DATA VECTORS

In Chapter II the conjecture was advanced that if simple structure basis vectors possess factorial invariance, then the matrix of principal axes M, of weighted data vectors would also be a factorially invariant matrix and would be more nearly invariant than the simple structure factor matrix. The basic reason for the hypothesis of more stability or invariance of factorial structure was that the principal axes are uniquely determined by all of the data vectors.

Tables 1 to 7 show various factor matrices for a set of body measurements used by Thurstone (1946) for teaching purposes because the data showed such a clear and interesting simple structure. The matrix of correlations was essentially non-negative, the highest negative correlation being -0.05; hence the correlation matrix is suitable for discussion here. Table 1 shows cosines of unweighted data vectors on the varimax simple structure factors. The varimax solution is presented instead of Thurstone's oblique solution because the factor pattern for the orthogonal varimax solution and Thurstone's oblique solution were identical using Thurstone's criterion for identity of factor pattern, a factor loading of no less than 0.35, with loadings between 0.30 and 0.35 being considered of doubtful significance and loadings below 0.30 being considered non-significant.

Table 5 shows matrix M, the matrix of coordinates on the principal axes of the weighted data vectors and Table 6 shows the cosines of the weighted data vectors on the principal axes of the weighted data vectors. Variable 9, head breadth, has the highest weighted invariance among the weighted data vectors. Visual inspection of Table 6 shows that variables 8 and 10, also head measurements, have very high cosines with variable 9 and with each other. Clearly variables 8, 9, and 10 are variables in a cluster with variable 9 as the first pivot vector. Of the remaining variables not in the first cluster, variable 12, hand breadth, has the highest weighted invariance value and is the second pivot vector therefore. Variables 5, span, and 11, hand length, obviously have substantial cosines with variable 12 and constitute the second cluster. Even if variable 5 is not included in the cluster, this is of no moment because it has a low weighted invariance value and hence cannot be a pivot vector for a cluster. The variable with the highest weighted invariance value not in the first two clusters is variable 2, sitting height, which obviously has a high cosine with variable 1, stature, again a variable with a very low weighted invariance value. The variable with the highest weighted invariance value not in the first three clusters is variable 7, chest depth, which clearly has high cosines with variables 3, 4, and 6, which are, respectively, shoulder breadth, hip breadth, and chest breadth. In this instance variables 2, 7, 9, and 12 constitute the most nearly orthogonal data basis for the unweighted data vectors.

It is noticeable that the varimax solution for the weighted data vectors, Table 2; the principal axis solution for the weighted vectors, matrix M, Table 5; the matrix of cosines on the principal axes of M, Table 6; and cosines on the basis of pivot vectors, Table 7; all identify the same vectors as belonging to clusters even though for Table 7 basis vectors 2 and 12 have a cosine of $-.899$. In the weighted data bases vectors of the basis serve only to group variables into clusters. Matrix M is the fundamental matrix for weighted data vectors; the other matrices deriving from M, shown in Tables 2, 6, and 7 are rearrangements of the row vectors of M useful only to facilitate interpretation. The basis vectors are not interpretable in factor analytic terms as hypothetical variables. They are not "factors" and in particular, negative entries are not interpretable in factorial terms. Tables 2, 6, and 7 all lead to the inference that there are four factors, one for long bones or intrinsic stature, one for girth, one for the extremities, and one for head size. These "factors" are, however, inferences or hypotheses and not basis vectors.

In Thurstone's solution, Table 1, the same factors are identified, but here they are basis vectors as well as inferences. It would seem, therefore, that here is an advantage because for example one can infer, as Thurstone did, that the extremity factor in part determines stature and span, whereas from the tables representing the weighted data vectors, it cannot reasonably be inferred that the factor called the extremity factor plays a role in determining stature although it can be inferred that it is associated with span. Also it can be inferred from the simple structure solution that the long bones factor and the extremity factor have something to do with span which seems entirely reasonable since span is experimentally dependent upon measures of the long arm bones, hand length, and shoulder breadth. From the weighted data vectors, however, it cannot be inferred that span is in part determined by the long bones factor; it seems rather that span is largely associated with the extremities factor, which appears unreasonable since hand length would seem to constitute a relatively small part of the variance of span.

This discrepancy in results bears close examination since the similarities between the two varimax solutions for the weighted and unweighted vectors is marked. Consideration of the discrepancies can begin by noting that variables 1 and 5 can both be considered as being factorially complex and that variable 5 has the highest cosine on the first principal axis of the unweighted data vectors while variable 1 has the third highest cosine; however variable 1 has rather considerably less of its variance accounted for by the first principal axis and considerably more of its variance accounted for by the second principal axis than does variable 5. The effect of the weighting is to accentuate but little the difference of the two variables on the first principal axis since the first principal axis receives minimum weight but to accentuate more the difference on the second principal axis. The rise in cosine on the extremity factor of the variable 5 and the drop in cosine of variable 1 on the extremity factor in the varimax solution for the weighted data vectors is therefore due in large part to accentuation of the second component of the first variable in the unweighted principal axes. Thus the cosine of .519 of variable 1, with the extremity factor for the unweighted data, is to a large extent determined by the second principal axis of the unweighted vectors. For variable 5, the rise in cosine is due to relatively low weighting given to the first two components of the vector on the principal axes and to the relatively high weighting given to the last two components, especially the last. The high cosines for both vectors in the unweighted varimax solutions derive from different principal axis components.

The weighting process then so operates as to cluster variables differentially according to their weighted similarity to principal axes. The weighting process minimizes successively the first components on the principal axes, then the second, etc. Contrariwise it might be stated that the weighting process maximizes successively the last principal axis components, the next-to-last principal axis components, etc.

The solution for the unweighted data vectors emphasizes the first and second components of both variables 1 and 5 whereas that for the weighted vectors emphasizes the second and third components for variable 1 and the last component for variable 5. Thus, when that which is common to all variables in $r, r - 1, \ldots, r - r + 1$ successive orthogonal subspaces is minimized, clustering indicates that as much as possible the cluster variables are accounted for by the same single component or principal axis. The low cosine for variable 1 on the extremity factor for the weighted vectors shows that what is common and most differentiating to variables 12, 11, and 5 is not common to variable 1. The relatively high cosine in the solution for the unweighted vectors indicates commonality between the variables due either to different principal axis components or to the same components, whether it is one or the other cannot be told from the size of the cosine. The weighting process so operates as to limit the value of cosines on the basis of both length and angle whereas the rotations of the unweighted vectors limit cosine values only on the basis of angular separation. In other words change of basis, starting with the principal axes, in the simple structure solution has the effect of distributing the latent roots among the basis vectors. The "roots" of other bases than the principal axes tend toward equality. This increases the variance of squared cosines on basis vectors. Minimizing principal axis components with respect to simple structure components amounts to minimizing variability in the rows of the transformation matrix carrying the principal axes to the simple structure basis. When the data are unweighted this amounts to minimizing cosines between simple structure factors and the principal axes. Weighting the data vectors gives two ways of minimizing the relationship between the simple structure factors and the principal axes. The two ways of minimizing are rotation and operations on the lengths of vectors.

Inspection of the transformation matrices carrying the principal axes of the weighted and unweighted vectors to their respective varimax bases shows that the variability of the rows of cosines, which express the principal axes in the new basis, is decidedly lower for the weighted than for the unweighted vectors. An index of total relative variability for two such matrices can be regarded as a measure of efficiency of purifying factors. An index of efficiency on a scale from zero to unity is

$$1 - \frac{\sum\limits_{1}^{r} s_i^2}{r - (1/r)} \tag{1}$$

where s_i^2 is the variance of the ith row of the transformation matrix and $1 - (1/r)$ is the maximal possible sum of the variances for the $r \times r$ transformation matrix. $1 - (1/r)$ is the value attained when the transformation matrix is an identity matrix.

As it is with the factors of factor analysis, so it is with the basis vectors for the vectors of S, the data matrix for classified behavior. If one uses unweighted data vectors, the best r data vectors for a data basis are those selected from the pivot vectors identified from matrix M. These will often, but not always, be the vectors of the most nearly orthogonal data basis. The vectors of the most nearly orthogonal data basis will always, however, have very high cosines with the unweighted vectors corresponding to the pivot vectors in M. When clusters of variables are to be used to determine the unweighted data basis, the best cluster vectors are those determined from M. As the analysis of the weighted data vectors shows, inference and hypothesis formation based on vectors with substantial inner products or cosines with more than one basis vector is an extremely complex affair and therefore hazardous.

TABLE 1*

VARIMAX SIMPLE STRUCTURE
UNWEIGHTED BODY MEASURES

		V_1	V_2	V_3	V_4	h^2
1	Stature	08	85	08	52	86
2	Sitting Height	10	97	19	10	76
3	Shoulder Breadth	17	30	88	33	33
4	Hip Breadth	03	15	92	35	55
5	Span	16	62	26	72	75
6	Chest Breadth	19	18	94	21	56
7	Chest Depth	−02	01	99	02	36
8	Head Length	87	18	43	15	38
9	Head Breadth	99	−05	−04	14	39
10	Head Height	98	17	−13	00	35
11	Hand Length	21	50	17	83	82
12	Hand Breadth	−01	08	42	90	60

* Decimal points are omitted.

TABLE 2*

VARIMAX SIMPLE STRUCTURE
WEIGHTED BODY MEASURES

	V_1	V_2	V_3	V_4
1	−15	95	−20	20
2	06	91	13	−40
3	42	03	89	−16
4	−21	17	97	01
5	−14	18	−28	93
6	13	03	96	−25
7	−10	04	92	−37
8	97	−09	23	−06
9	97	08	08	−21
10	98	−03	−19	−03
11	−04	−25	−38	89
12	−28	−61	−08	74

* Decimal points omitted.

TABLE 3*

VARIMAX TRANSFORMATION MATRIX
(UNWEIGHTED VECTORS)

	V_1	V_2	V_3	V_4
P_1	58	−50	23	−60
P_2	54	83	04	−14
P_3	−12	07	97	19
P_4	59	−26	−05	76

* Decimal points omitted.

TABLE 4*

VARIMAX TRANSFORMATION MATRIX
(WEIGHTED VECTORS)

	V_1	V_2	V_3	V_4
M_1	76	34	29	−47
M_2	−63	44	49	42
M_3	07	−64	76	12
M_4	11	54	32	77

* Decimal points omitted.

TABLE 5

MATRIX OF COORDINATES, M, OF WEIGHTED DATA
VECTORS ON PRINCIPAL AXES

	Weighted Body Measures				Unweighted Invariance	Weighted Invariance
	M_1	M_2	M_3	M_4		
1	.16	1.04	−2.38	1.85	10.17	1.62
2	4.03	4.09	−3.61	1.58	48.44	15.09
3	2.57	.98	2.55	.89	14.87	4.62
4	.22	1.99	3.14	.76	14.47	3.19
5	−1.45	−.94	−.59	1.84	6.74	1.46
6	2.15	2.18	2.96	.64	18.56	5.28
7	2.06	3.76	3.46	.14	30.35	8.52
8	4.57	−2.92	1.64	.53	32.35	12.59
9	6.23	−3.16	.32	.12	48.91	20.68
10	4.85	−4.88	−.41	.09	47.52	17.88
11	−2.70	−2.70	−.09	1.78	17.76	5.66
12	−5.37	−2.96	2.69	1.28	46.43	17.25

TABLE 6*

Cosines of Weighted Data Vectors
on Principal Axes

	M_1	M_2	M_3	M_4
1	05	32	−73	56
2	58	59	−52	23
3	67	25	66	23
4	06	52	83	20
5	−56	−36	−23	71
6	50	51	69	15
7	37	68	63	03
8	80	−51	29	09
9	89	−45	05	02
10	70	−71	−06	01
11	−64	−64	−02	42
12	−83	−43	40	19

* Decimal points omitted.

TABLE 7

Cosines of Pivot Vectors
with Weighted Data Vectors

	$\overline{9}$	$\overline{2}$	$\overline{7}$	$\overline{12}$
1	20	72	−21	−36
2	23	1.00	30	−90
3	43	24	84	−36
4	−14	−04	90	−05
5	−33	−26	−52	66
6	25	26	96	−39
7	05	30	1.00	−35
8	96	04	13	−31
9	1.00	23	05	−57
10	95	03	30	−30
11	−18	−64	−68	88
12	−57	−90	−35	1.00
$\overline{9}$	1.00	23	05	−57
$\overline{2}$	23	1.00	30	−90
$\overline{7}$	23	30	1.00	−35
$\overline{12}$	−57	−90	−35	1.00

REFERENCES

Arrow, K. J. *Social Choice and Individual Values*. New York: Wiley, 1951.

Auld, F. J., Jr. & Murray, E. J. Content-analysis studies of psychotherapy. *Psychol. Bull.* 1950, **52**, 378–395.

Berelson, B. *Content Analysis in Communication Research*. Glencoe, Illinois: Free Press, 1952.

Bock, D. The selection of judges for preference testing. *Psychometrika*, 1956, **21**, 349–366.

Brice, N. The facilitation and obstruction of progress in psychotherapy: a statistical analysis of a single case. Unpublished doctoral dissertation, Univer. of Chicago, 1957.

Butler, J. M. Empty research proposal: category analysis. *Univer. of Chicago Counseling Center Staff Paper*, 1951.

Butler, J. M. Measuring the effectiveness of counseling and psychotherapy. *Pers. & Guid. J.*, 1953, 88–92.

Butler, J. M. The analysis of successive sets of behavior data. *Univer. of Chicago Counseling Center Discussion Papers*, Univer. of Chicago Lib., Vol. **1**, #1, 1955.

Butler, J. M. On the structure of groups and institutions. *Univer. of Chicago Counseling Center Discussion Papers*, Univer. of Chicago Lib., Vol. **2**, #13, 1956.

Butler, J. M. An orthogonalization computing method for successive set analysis. *Univer. of Chicago Counseling Center Discussion Papers*, Univer. of Chicago Lib., Vol. **6**, #5, 1959.

Butler, J. M.   Client-centered therapy.   In L. Abt & D. Brower (Eds.), *Progress in Clinical Psychology III*, New York: Grune & Stratton, 1959.

Butler, J. M.   Introduction to successive set analysis.   *Univer. of Chicago Counseling Center Discussion Papers*, Univer. of Chicago Lib., Vol. 5, #16, 1959.

Butler, J. M.   Orthogonalization processes for oblique simple structures.   *Univer. of Chicago Counseling Center Discussion Papers*, Univer. of Chicago Lib., Vol. 5, #5, 1959.

Butler, J. M. & Rice, Laura.   Self-actualization, new experience, and psychotherapy.   *Univer. of Chicago Counseling Center Discussion Papers*, Univer. of Chicago Lib., Vol. 6, #12, 1960.

Butler, J. M. & Wagstaff, Alice.   A standard form for classification systems in successive set analysis.   *Univer. of Chicago Counseling Center Discussion Papers*, Univer. of Chicago Lib., Vol. 5, #7, 1959.

Cartwright, D. S., Kirtner, W. & Fox, Sophie.   An operator-display analysis of psychotherapy.   *Univer. of Chicago Counseling Center Discussion Papers*, Univer. of Chicago Lib., Vol. 2, #17, 1956.

Coombs, C. H., Raiffa, H., & Thrall, R. M.   Some views on mathematical models and measurement theory.   *Psychol. Rev.*, 1954, 61, 132–144.

Coombs, C. H. & Kao, R. C.   Non-metric factor analysis.   *Univer. of Mich. Eng. Res. Inst. Bull.*, 1955, #38.

Coombs, C. H.   A theory of data.   *Psychol. Rev.*, 1960, 67, 143–159.

Crowder, N. A.   A constructive definition of simple structure in factor analysis.   Paper read at annual meeting of Amer. Psychol. Assn., 1955.

Dollard, J. M. & Mowrer, O. H.   A method of measuring tension in written documents.   *J. abnorm. soc. Psychol.*, 1947, 42, 3–32.

Fox, Margaret.   A quantitative study of changes in verbal behavior occurring in client-centered counseling.   Unpublished doctoral dissertation, Univer. of Chicago, 1951.

Gibson, W. A.   Application of the mathematics of multiple factor analysis to problems of latent structure analysis.   Unpublished doctoral dissertation, Univer. of Chicago, 1951.

Gibson, W. A.   Orthogonal and oblique simple structures.   *Psychometrika*, 1952, **17**, 317–323.

Green, B. F.   The orthogonal approximation of an oblique structure in factor analysis.   *Psychometrika*, 1952, **17**, 429–440.

Green, B. F.   A general solution for the latent class model of latent structure analysis.   *Psychometrika*, 1953, **16**, 151–166.

Guttman, L.   The quantification of a class of attributes: a theory and method of scale construction.   In Horst, P. (Ed.), *The Prediction of Personal Adjustment*.   New York, S.S.R.C., 1941.

Holzinger, K. J. & Harman, H.   *Factor Analysis*.   Chicago: Univer. of Chicago Press, 1953.

Hood, W. C. & Koopmans, T. C. (Eds.), *Studies in Econometric Method*, New York: Wiley, 1953.

Koopmans, T. C.   Identification problems in latent structure analysis.   *Cowles Commission Discussion Paper*, 1951.

Lazarsfeld, P.   *Mathematical Thinking in the Social Sciences*.   Glencoe, Illinois: Free Press, 1957.

Lasswell, H. D.   A provisional classification of symbol data.   *Psychiat.*, 1938, **1**, 197–204.

Lasswell, H. D., Leites, N. & Assoc. (Eds.), *Language of Politics*, New York: Stewart, 1949.

Rice, Laura, Wagstaff, Alice, & Butler, J. M.   Successive set project: Part I: preliminary analysis of data from one dimension of client category system.   *Univer. of Chicago Counseling Center Discussion Papers*.   Univer. of Chicago Lib., Vol. **5**, #4, 1959.

Simmel, Marianne & Counts, Sarah.   Some stable response determinants of perception, thinking, and learning: a study based on the analysis of a single test.   *Genet. Psychol. Monogr.*, 1957, **56**, 3–157.

Simon, H. A.   Logic of causal relations.   *Cowles Commission Discussion Papers*, New series #70, 1952.

Simon, H. A.   Causal ordering and identifiability.   In Hood, W. & Koopmans, T. (Eds.), *Studies in Econometric Method*.   New York: Wiley, 1953.

Tate, F. K.   A rank pattern analysis of verbal behavior in client-centered psychotherapy.   Unpublished doctoral dissertation, Univer. of Chicago, 1953.

Thurstone, L. L.   Factor analysis and body types.   *Psychometrika*, 1946, **11**, 15–21.

Thurstone, L. L.   *Multiple Factor Analysis*.   Chicago: Univer. of Chicago Press, 1947.

Wagstaff, Alice & Butler, J. M. A summary matrix for successive set analysis. *Univer. of Chicago Counseling Center Discussion Papers*, The Univer. of Chicago Lib., Vol. **5**, #9, 1959.

Wagstaff, Alice.   Successive set analysis of verbal styles in psychotherapy.   Unpublished doctoral dissertation, Univer. of Chicago, 1959.

White, R. K.   Black boy: a value analysis.   *J. abnorm. soc. Psychol.*, 1947, **42**, 440–461.

Yule, G. U. & Kendall, M. G.   *An introduction to the theory of statistics.*   (13th ed.) London: Griffin, 1953.

INDEX

Achievement tests, 92
Alternatives, selection of, 8–9
Analysis:
  of augmented matrix, 66
  of data matrix, 35–39
  of empirical classification systems,
    11–46
  exploratory, 52–53, 67–91
    Halstead Category Test, 67–75, 90
    political attitudes study, 86–89
    psychotherapy verbal style study,
      76–85, 90, 91
    weighting behavior, 52–53
  factor, 25, 30, 34, 37, 40–42, 45, 65,
    68, 90–91, 103, 106, 107–110
    communalities, 40–42, 45, 65, 103
    in exploratory analysis, 90–91
    factorial invariance, 25, 30, 34, 106
    weighted data vectors, 107–110
  latent class, 65, 102–105
Answer pattern, 47
Anxiety scale (Taylor), 83
Aptitude tests, 92
Attitude inventories, 92
Attrition cases, 76

Barron ego-strength scale, 84
Bartlett, 4
Basis vectors, 14, 17–19, 20, 21, 27–28,
    32, 43, 44, 62, 65, 69, 79, 92–94,
    98, 105
  orthogonal, 17–19, 20, 21, 69, 79, 98
  orthonormal, 18–19, 32, 65
  tests of significance for number of,
    92–94

Behavior:
  matrix, 25
  observation, 2–4, 11. (*See also*
    Naturalistic observation)
  space, 16, 17
  vectors, 11, 52
  verbal. (*See* Psychotherapy verbal
    style study)
  weighting, 52–53
Bisection, 58
Bock, D., 94, 114
Boolean "and" vector, 63, 65
Boundary vectors, 18, 20, 23, 28, 33,
    42, 45, 66
  unweighted, 33
  weighting, effect of, 45
Boyle, Robert, 1

Central vectors, 22, 23, 28
Centroids, 56, 62
Centroid vectors, 86
Characteristic vector, 35, 36
Chi-square statistic, 14
Classification systems:
  alternatives, selection of, 8–9
  answer pattern, 47
  best data basis, 17–19
    rule for finding, 19
  categories of observation, 3–4
  classifying aspects of a response,
    47–48
  coarse-grained, 7
  coding data, 12–14
  creativity in construction of, 8
  criteria for, 5–6

Classification systems (*Cont.*):
dichotomous classification, 102–105
empirical, 11–46
arrangement of data, 12–14
assessment of internal productivity, 14–18
best data basis, 19
communalities, 40–42, 45
coordinates, 20–21
Q-transformation, 39–40
simplest basis, 21–26, 27, 29, 30,
33, 34, 45
types and traits, 34–35
weighted data vectors and bases,
26–34, 45–46
exhaustiveness, 7
external productivity, 6, 7, 9–10,
76–85, 90, 91
psychotherapy verbal style study,
76–85, 90, 91
fine-grained, 6–7, 10
function of, 5–6
higher order vectors, 63–66
internal productivity, 6, 7, 9–10, 11,
14–18, 21, 26, 40, 44, 54, 55, 66,
76–85, 86–87, 90–91
assessment of, 14–18
behavior space, 16, 17
index of, 26, 40, 44, 66, 79, 87
matrix defining, 54, 55
most invariant basis, 21
political attitudes study, 86–87
psychotherapy verbal style study,
76–85, 90, 91
mutual exclusivity of, 6, 9, 14
normative decisions, 90–91
principal axis method, 22, 25, 27–35,
45
psychotherapy verbal style study,
76–85, 90, 91
remainder class, 7
sub-categories, 6, 7, 15, 66, 90–91,
92–94, 102
preferential selection of, 15
subjective element, 4–5, 6, 7–8, 10, 91
"unclassifiable" class, 7
Cluster vectors, 24, 25, 30–31, 34, 110
computing routine, 31
defined, 30–31
Coarse-grained classification system, 7

Coding, 12–14
Column vectors, 15, 25. (*See also*
Row vectors)
Communalities, 40–42, 45, 65
Computer, digital, 69
Counting activity, 72–75
Counts, Sarah, 67–68, 75, 116
Creativity, in construction of classifi-
cation systems, 8

Darwin, Charles, 1
Data:
arrangement of, 12–14
behavior, 11
best data basis, 17–19
coding, 12–14
matrix, 12–14, 35–39, 47–49
analysis of, 35–39
not in standard form, 47–49
recording of, 5
simplest basis, 21–26, 27, 29, 30, 33,
34, 45
vectors, 16–19, 20, 22, 23, 26–34, 40,
45, 46, 106–113
unweighted, 32, 33, 34, 46
weighted, 26–34, 45, 106–113
Dichotomy, 90, 102–105
Digital computer, 69

Easton, David, 86
Ego-strength scale (Barron), 84
Einstein, Albert, 1
Empirical classification systems, 11–46
arrangement of data, 12–14
assessment of internal productivity,
14–18
best data basis, 19
communalities, 40–42, 45
coordinates, 20–21
Q-transformation, 39–40
simplest basis, 21–26, 27, 29, 30, 33,
34, 45
types and traits, 34–35
weighted data vectors and bases,
26–34, 45–46
Epilepsy, 67
Exhaustive classification systems, 7

Exploratory analysis:
  applications, 67–91
    Halstead Category Test, 67–75, 90
    political attitudes study, 86–89
    psychotherapy verbal style study, 76–85, 90, 91
  factor analysis in, 90–91
  weighting behavior, 52–53
External productivity, 6, 7, 9–10, 83–85

Fabre, Jean Henri, 8
Factor analysis, 25, 30, 34, 37, 40–42, 45, 65, 68, 90–91, 103, 106, 107–110
  communalities, 40–42, 45, 65, 103
  in exploratory analysis, 90–91
  factorial invariance, 25, 30, 34, 106
  weighted data vectors, 107–110
Factorial invariance, 25, 30, 34, 106
Fine-grained classification system, 6–7, 10
Fleming, Alexander, 1
Freud, Sigmund, 4

Gibson, W. A., 56, 102, 115, 116
Gram-Schmidt orthogonalization process, 95
Graphical rotation, 54, 69
Green, B. F., 54, 55, 60–62, 102, 116

Halstead Category Test, 67–75, 90
  counting activity, 72–75
Hess, Robert D., 86
Hook, L. Harmon, 95

Identity matrix, 95–101, 110
Index of internal productivity, 26, 40, 44, 66, 79, 87
Internal productivity, 6, 7, 9–10, 11, 14–18, 21, 26, 40, 44, 54, 55, 66, 76–85, 86–87, 90–91
  assessment of, 14–18
    behavior space, 16, 17
    chi-square statistic, 14

Internal productivity (Cont.):
  assessment of (Cont.):
    preferential selection of sub-classes, 15
  index of, 26, 40, 44, 66, 79, 87
  matrix defining, 54, 55
  most invariant basis, 21
  political attitudes study, 86–87
  psychotherapy verbal style study, 76–85, 90, 91
Item-score matrix, 12

Koopmans, T. C., 65, 116

Latent class analysis, 65, 102–105
Latent vector, 52, 93
Lazarsfeld, P., 102, 116
Least-squares methods, 52, 55–56, 60–62, 93–94
Loadings, of responses, 69–73, 85, 88
  Halstead Category Test, 69–73
  political attitudes study, 88
  psychotherapy verbal style study, 85
Lobectomy, 67

Matrices:
  augmented, analysis of, 66
  behavior, 25
  configurational invariance, 21
  of coordinates, 21–26, 27, 29, 30, 33, 34, 45
  of correlation, 106
  data, 12–14, 35–39, 47–49
    analysis of, 35–39
    not in standard form, 47–49
  defining internal productivity, 54, 55
  derived by hypothesis, 50
  higher order, 63–66
  identity, 95–101, 110
  item-score, 12
  orthogonal transformation, 32
  remainder, 37
  square symmetric, 78
  transformation, 110, 112
  unit rank, 36
Maze, 8

Naturalistic observation, 1, 2–10, 11,
    90–91. (*See also* Classification
    systems)
  of behavior, 2–4, 11
    purpose of, 11
  behavioral structure of an occasion, 3
  function of, 5
  problems of, 5
  psychotherapeutic interviews, 90
  recording of data, 5
  sequence of occasions, 3
  sets of occasions, 3
  subjective element, 4–5, 6, 7–8, 10, 91
Newton, Isaac, 1
Normative decisions, 90–91
n-tuple, 11

Oblique bases, 17, 18–19, 33, 34, 43,
    44, 54–62
  orthogonal basis approximating sim-
    plest, 43, 44, 54–62
Observation. (*See* Naturalistic obser-
    vation and Classification sys-
    tems)
Organism-environment transaction, 7
Orthogonal bases, 17–19, 20, 21–22, 23,
    24, 26, 27, 30, 33, 34, 39, 43, 44,
    54–62, 69, 79, 86, 94, 98
  approximating oblique simplest basis,
    43, 44, 54–62
  vectors, 17–19, 20, 21, 26–27, 39,
    69, 79, 98
Orthogonalization, 59–62, 79, 95, 105
  Gram-Schmidt process, 95
  process of, 59–62
Orthonormal basis, 18–19, 32, 65, 95–97
  vectors, 18–19, 32, 65
Outside vectors, 18. (*See also* Bound-
    ary vectors)

Parallelogram law, 57
Personality inventories, 92
Pivot vectors, 22, 23, 24, 31–32
Political attitudes study, 86–89
Principal axis, 22, 25, 27–35, 45
Productivity. (*See* External produc-
    tivity and Internal productivity)

Psychotherapy verbal style study, 76–
    85, 90, 91
  external productivity, assessing,
    83–85
  involvement, 77
  level of expression, 77
  quality of participation, 78

Q-transformation, 39–40, 44, 46, 53

Reference factors, 38
Remainder class, 7
Remainder matrix, 37
Rogin, Michael, 86, 87
Rotation, graphical, 54, 69
Row vectors, 15, 23, 25, 32, 35

Scaling, 52–53
Sequence of occasions, 3
Simmel, Marianne, 67–68, 75, 116
Simplest basis vectors, 21–26, 27, 29,
    30, 33, 34, 38, 45
Simplex, 90
Subject-environment transactions, 68
Subjective element, in observation,
    4–5, 6, 7–8, 10, 91
Symmetry, 60, 98

Taylor Anxiety Scale, 83
Tests:
  achievement, 92
  aptitude, 92
  attitude, 92
  Halstead Category, 67–75, 90
  for number of basis vectors, 92–94
  personality, 92
  political attitudes, 86–89
  psychotherapy verbal style, 76–85,
    90, 91
Thurstone, L. L., 21, 34, 38, 57, 106,
    107–108, 117
Transformation matrices, 110, 112
Transformations, Q, 39–40, 44, 46, 53

"Unclassifiable" class, 7

Varimax, 106, 111, 112
Vectors:
  basis, 14, 17–19, 20, 21, 27–28, 32, 43, 44, 62, 65, 69, 79, 92–94, 98, 105
    orthogonal, 17–19, 20, 21, 69, 79, 98
    orthonormal, 18–19, 32, 65
    tests of significance for number of, 92–94
  behavioral, 11, 52
  Boolean "and" vector, 63, 65
  boundary, 18, 20, 23, 28, 33, 42, 45, 66
    unweighted, 33
    weighting, effect of, 45
  central, 22, 23, 28
  centroid, 86
  characteristic, 35, 36
  cluster, 24, 25, 30–31, 34, 110
    computing routines, 31
    defined, 30–31
  column, 15, 25. (*See also* Row vectors)
  data, 16–19, 20, 22, 23, 26–34, 40, 45, 46, 106–113
    unweighted, 32, 33, 34, 46
    weighted, 26–34, 45, 106–113

Vectors (*Cont.*):
  higher order, 63–66
  latent, 52, 93
  n-tuple, 11
  orthogonal, 17–19, 20, 21, 26–27, 39, 69, 79, 98
  orthonormal, 18–19, 32, 65
  outside, 18. (*See also* Boundary vectors)
  pivot, 22, 23, 24, 31–32
  principal axis, 36
  row, 15, 23, 25, 32, 35
  simplest basis, 21–26, 27, 29, 30, 33, 34, 38, 45
  weighted data, 26–34
Verbal behavior. (*See* Psychotherapy verbal style study)

Wagstaff, Alice, 78, 115, 116, 117
Weighting, 26–34, 45–46, 52–53, 93–94, 106–113
  behavior, 52–53
  boundary vectors, 45
  column, 29–30
  data vectors, 26–34, 45–46, 106–113
  row, 29–30
  for subjects, 52–53
Wrigley, Charles, 27